Dickie Davies'
SPORTS
QUIZ ☆ BOOK

Dickie Davies'
SPORTS
QUIZ ☆ BOOK

B⬢XTREE

First published in the UK 1992
by BOXTREE LIMITED, 36 Tavistock Street,
London WC2E 7PB

10 9 8 7 6 5 4 3 2 1

ISBN: 1-85283-694-6

Cover design by Titan Studio
Typeset by DP Photosetting, Aylesbury, Bucks

Printed and bound in Great Britain by
Cox & Wyman Ltd., Reading, Berkshire

A catalogue record for this book is available from the
British Library

Contents

Introduction

Hello to all you sports fans . . . welcome to the *Dickie Davies' Sports Quiz Book*. I hope you enjoy it.

I have been involved with sport for many years now, but it never ceases to amaze me that, week after week, some record is broken, a hilarious incident happens or a colourful new character emerges.

The world of sport is never boring. There is always something bizarre, funny or superhuman happening somewhere . . . but the record books do not always tell you that.

The aim of this collection of almost 1,000 questions is to reflect the unusual side of sporting competition . . . as well as quizzing you about achievements of countries, teams and individuals.

With more than 30 sections, there should be something for everyone, from the most familiar, everyday sports . . . to the frankly obscure!

One thing I guarantee – the questions in this book were not thought up to give you an easy time, but I know from my T.V. programme *Sportsmasters* how knowledgeable so many of you are. So delve deep into your sporting knowledge . . . and GOOD LUCK!

The Questions

General - Part 1

• QUESTIONS •

1 Who was the first woman to participate in the Oxford-Cambridge University boat race?

2 How many hits score a win in men's fencing?

3 What is an ice hockey puck made of?

4 What restrictions are there on horses entered for the Oaks?

5 What does the TT stand for in the Isle of Man's motorcycle races?

6 Only three riders have won the Tour de France five times – two were French, what nationality was the other?

7 Which baseball team has won the World Series most times?

8 Which darts player said: "A good darts player who can count always beats a brilliant darts player who can't."?

9 Who was the Home Secretary who requested that the England cricket side did not tour South Africa in 1970?

10 What is a Canadian Pairs race?

11 Maidstone Tigresses, Doncaster Belles and Red Star Southampton play which sport?

12 What is crown green bowling?

13 What, traditionally, is the most heavily gambled-upon race in the British horse racing calendar?

14 What disciplines make up the modern pentathlon event?

15 At which sport did Julian Snow beat Chris Bray to win the Champagne Laurent-Perrier Masters in May 1992?

16 Former USA president Ronald Reagan was a reporter in which sport?

17 Which sport does the Federation Internationale d'Escrime oversee?

18 In horse racing, what is a maiden?

19 What is the name of the World's biggest football stadium, which holds 200,000 fans?

20 How often is yachting's Admiral's Cup raced?

21 What British National Championships were held at Burnham-on-sea in March 1992?

22 What do Fives players use to hit the ball?

23 With which country did Sri Lanka draw a Test cricket series in 1990–91?

24 With which sport do you associate "skeet"?

25 Red Rum was denied a hat-trick of Grand National wins by which horse in 1975?

26 What do Giovanna Amati, Davina Galica and Lella Lombardi have in common?

27 Between February 15 and February 19, 1992, England beat France in full internationals at three sports – what were they?

28 Why did Italian television's RAI station halt coverage of sporting events involving national heroes boxer Francesco Damiani, runner Gelindo Bordin and tennis player Paolo Cane in early 1992?

29 When did Ireland's Stephen Roche first win the Tour de France?

30 At what sport did Earl's Court beat Wandsworth in the British Grand Final in 1991?

Football – Part 1

• QUESTIONS •

1 Name the four Football League clubs that Kevin Keegan played for?

2 Which is the only non-English club to have won the FA Cup?

3 Where would you be if you were watching a match at the Nou Camp stadium?

4 Which two League clubs play home matches at St James' Park?

5 Who were Graeme Souness' five predecessors as managers of Liverpool?

6 Who scored the only goal in the 1973 FA Cup final?

7 Arbroath hold the British scoring record with a 36-0 Scottish Cup victory over which unfortunate club?

8 Two record transfers, involving £11.7 million, moved which international star around the globe in 1982 and 1984?

9 During the 1980s the First Division Championship was wrested away from Merseyside only twice – by which clubs and in which years?

10 Which Scottish club plays at Easter Road?

11 Who was installed as England's caretaker manager after Sir Alf Ramsey was sacked in 1973?

12 Up until 1992, only four clubs had won the Scottish Premier Division – who were they?

13 Which team prevented Celtic from winning their second European Cup by beating them in the 1970 Final?

14 Until Howard Wilkinson was appointed as manager in 1988, Leeds United were managed through the decade by three former Leeds players – who were they?

15 Name the star, who Pele once described as "The greatest footballer in the world"?

16 Who failed in his application for the manager's jobs of England (1977), Scotland (1985), Eire (1985) and Wales (1988)?

17 Which player was bought by Arsenal for £1 million and then sold on to Queen's Park Rangers without making a single League appearance for the Gunners?

18 Whose back-heeled goal in a 1974 Manchester derby consigned United to relegation to the Second Division?

19 Dave Beasant made the first ever FA Cup Final penalty save – who made the second?

20 Which Midlands club rallies to the cry of "Come on you Baggies!"?

21 Who beat Moscow Dynamo 3–2 in the 1972 Cup Winners' Cup Final to win their first European trophy?

22 After being elected to the First Division in 1892, Newton Heath went on to achieve worldwide fame following a name change to what?

23 Where and what year did England play their last home match NOT to be staged at Wembley?

24 Who is the only manager to lead two different British clubs to European Cup Winners' Cup Final victories?

25 Who won the first League Cup Final to be staged at Wembley?

26 "The Crazy Gang have beaten the Culture Club!" Who said this about which occasion?

27 Which club plays at Gigg Lane?

28 What is the Italian first division called?

29 Who were the beaten semi-finalists in the FA Cup of 1990–91?

30 What first did Coventry City achieve on January 6, 1992?

Rugby Union
• QUESTIONS •

1 Name the national stadia of all the Five Nations teams.

2 What is the USA's rugby team known as?

3 Which was the only side to beat the All Blacks on their 1963–64 tour in Britain?

4 Who was the top points scorer in the 1991 World Cup?

5 What is the lowest number of tries scored by a country in a Grand Slam winning campaign?

6 Which player was named as the British Lions Player of the Series after the successful 1989 tour of Australia?

7 In which year was the Rugby Football Union formed?

8 Which two England players could have capped their 1992 Grand Slam campaigns with a try in each match if they had managed to score in the final game, against Wales, at Twickenham.

9 Brothers, Steve and Graham Bachop both played in the 1991 World Cup tournament, but for different countries. Who did they play for and in what positions?

10 Who is the all time record points scorer in international rugby?

11 Which two former England Number Eights are now more comfortable rowing together at international events than in the middle of a ruck?

12 Against which country did Ireland suffer two shock international defeats in July, 1991?

13 Who was the first team captain to get his hands on the Webb Ellis Trophy?

14 What emblem do France have on their shirts?

15 In late 1990, which club ended Neath's run of 51 consecutive wins over Welsh sides?

16 Which rugby team share the same nickname as football's Southampton and Rugby League's St Helens?

17 Who was the only English forward to score a try in the 1991 World Cup?

18 Which player was selected to go on the 1989 Lions tour of Australia before he had been capped by his country at full international level?

19 In 1957, 110,000 fans turned out to watch an international match involving France ... and which other nation?

20 What caused the rift between France and the home nations, leading to the French pulling out of the competition in 1932 and not returning until 1947?

21 Who was the first England player to score a try in every match of a Five Nations championship?

22 Which Oxford University, Rosslyn Park and England winger became the first international player to lose his life in World War II?

23 Where and when was the last time that Rugby was an Olympic sport ... and which country is the reigning Olympic champion?

24 Why does the Bath full-back always wear a number 16 shirt, instead of the position's usual number 15?

25 What is the oldest annual fixture on the rugby calendar?

26 On what sporting subject other than rugby has the great Welsh scrum-half Gareth Edwards written a book?

27 Who was England's captain during their 1987 World Cup campaign?

28 Who was the only England player to be dropped during the outstanding 1992 Grand Slam success?

29 Who won the first ever women's Rugby World Cup, staged in Wales, in 1991?

30 In the 1991–92 season, a detective inspector was sent off for doing "a tap dance" on a police constable's head during an international match. Name the players and the match.

Motor Sport

• QUESTIONS •

1 How many times did Stirling Moss win the Formula One World Drivers' Championship?

2 At which circuit were 83 spectators killed in an horrific accident in 1955?

3 Before the 1992 race at Kyalami, when the last time a Formula One Grand Prix was held in South Africa?

4 Who built the car which Jack Brabham drove to the 1966 World Drivers' Championship?

5 Who was the last winning rider in the Isle of Man senior TT race to average less than 100mph and in which year?

6 Which driver lost his life in a pile-up involving 11 cars at Monza in the 1978 Italian Grand Prix?

7 Which driver won the Monte Carlo and Lombard RAC rallies in 1991 and the Safari Rally in 1992?

8 The great Fangio won the most Formula One World Drivers' Championships – what nationality was he?

9 Who is the only South African to have won the Formula One World Drivers' Championships and what team did he drive for?

10 When and where was the first Grand Prix race?

11 Graham Hill shared his surname with a 1960s Grand Prix winner. Who?

12 Which engines have powered the most cars to Formula One victory?

13 John Surtees was the 1964 World Drivers' Champion, but he was also three times World Motorcycling Champion at two engine sizes – which two?

14 At which circuit was Niki Lauda involved in the horrific fireball crash which left him severely scarred . . . and who was the driver who saved his life?

15 What prompted France's two times World Sportscar champion Jean-Louis Schlesser to say in 1992 "Formula One is becoming a sport for dwarves."?

16 In which country did James Hunt clinch his only Formula One World Drivers' Championship?

17 Which Formula One driver was jailed in 1991 for spraying CS gas at a taxi driver following a traffic accident in London?

18 Which reigning world champion died in a road accident near Guildford in early 1959, just two months after retiring from Formula One?

19 Where is the Portuguese Grand Prix usually raced?

20 Who said about motor racing "In my sport, the quick are only listed among the dead."?

21 Which aptly named driver won the Brazilian Grand Prix in 1975, the first time he had raced in front of his home crowd?

22 In which city did the legendary Mille Miglia race start and where did it finish?

23 Which was the first British car to win the World Sportscar Championships?

24 Who was the only driver to win the Formula One World Drivers' Championship posthumously?

25 What tragic link was there between Ian Young, Roy Anderson, Frank Duffy and Petr Hlavatka in 1991?

26 Which team has won the Formula One Constructors Cup most times?

27 In 1965, British drivers were first, second and third in the Formula One World Drivers' Championship . . . name them.

28 Why was the Paris-Madrid race halted by organisers at Bordeaux in 1903?

29 Wayne Rainey, Michael Doohan and Kevin Schwantz between them won 14 of the 15 motorcycling Grand Prix in 1991 . . . who won the other?

30 Lella Lombardi became the first and only woman to win Formula One World Drivers' Championship points in which 1975 Grand Prix?

Athletics - Part 1

• QUESTIONS •

1. In the 800 metres, what is the last instruction given by the starter before the gun fires?

2. What was Liz McColgan's maiden name?

3. What does IAAF stand for?

4. Which is the shortest track event where the runners are allowed to break lanes?

5. Steve Ovett, Jack Buckner and Tim Hutchings swept the board in which event in the 1986 European Championships?

6. What was unusual about the finish of the first London Marathon?

7. Which well known athlete died in Wei-Fang, China, in 1945?

8. In 1986, which female athletes held the world records for 1,500 metres and the mile?

9. How long exactly is a marathon?

10. Name the three different Olympic throwing events for women.

11. At what average speed is someone running to complete a four minute mile?

12. How many laps in an indoor 800 metres race?

13 Which modern day "marathon" man won an Olympic gold medal in the Melbourne 1956 games?

14 Who ran the first 1,500 metres under three minutes and 30 seconds?

15 Who ran the last leg of the historic men's 4 × 400 metres relay in the 1991 World Championships in Tokyo, securing gold for Great Britain?

16 In relay races, how long is the takeover zone?

17 Who was known as "Yifter the Shifter"?

18 Which high jumper gave his name to a special kind of jumping technique?

19 What is Sebastian Coe's middle name?

20 What is the governing body of athletics in the USA called?

21 Which is the world's oldest annual marathon?

22 Which nation provided the winner of both the men's and women's 1,500 metres at the 1991 World Championships in Tokyo?

23 Who was the first women's javelin world champion?

24 Who won the first three world championships at the 110 metres hurdles?

25 Who said: "I don't call it cheating. Cheating is doing something nobody else is doing."?

26 What is usually the final event of an athletics championships?

27 With which event do you associate Sergei Bubka?

28 Who was the first British athlete to win the Olympic 100 metres title?

29 Who won gold for Great Britain in the 1991 European Championship 1,500 metres?

30 What is Universiade also known as?

Boxing

• QUESTIONS •

1 Who relieved Barry McGuigan of his WBA feather-weight title in 1986?

2 What is a bolo?

3 To be an undisputed world champion, what four titles does a boxer have to win?

4 Lennox Lewis won the Olympic super-heavyweight gold medal at the 1988 games in Seoul – which country was he boxing for?

5 Who was the only British boxer to go the full distance with all-time great, Joe Louis?

6 Which British boxer took just 161 days to win a Lonsdale belt in 1991, smashing the previous record by 42 days?

7 By what name is John Sholto Douglas better known?

8 At what weight did Muhammad Ali (as Cassius Clay) win Olympic gold in the 1960 Rome games?

9 Who did Britain's Colin McMillan beat to win the vacant Commonwealth featherweight title in January 1992?

10 What is the upper weight limit for a light heavyweight boxer?

11 In 1991, Thomas Hearns won his sixth world title. Two of those titles were in the same weight division – which division?

12 Who did Mike Tyson beat to become undisputed heavyweight champion of the world in 1987?

13 In which round of a 1990 British and European heavyweight title fight did Lennox Lewis end Gary Mason's boxing career?

14 Which promoter's run of having a hand in every single world heavyweight title fight since 1978 came to an end when he was not involved in the 1991 Evander Holyfield – George Foreman bout?

15 Why was Mikhail Gorbachev made an honorary member of the World Boxing Council in 1992?

16 Up until the end of 1991, Frank Bruno had lost to three world heavyweight champions in his career – who were they?

17 What handicap did 1920s middleweight champion Harry Greb, suffer from?

18 What is the lightest boxing division?

19 Who was the heaviest world heavyweight champion of all time?

20 Britain's Lloyd Honeyghan holds the record for the quickest knockout in a world title fight . . . who did he knock out and how long did it take?

21 Who was Chris Eubank talking about when he said: "I really hate him. That strut, that shoulder back stance. He makes me cringe."?

22 Who was the only boxer to go the distance twice with undefeated world heavyweight champion Rocky Marciano?

23 What pets did Mike Tyson used to keep when he was young?

24 Sugar Ray Robinson won the world middleweight championship five times . . . at what other weight did he win a world title?

25 The shooting of which promoter led to the trial for attempted murder, and acquittal, of former world junior welterweight champion, Terry Marsh?

26 In which city did James "Buster" Douglas sensationally beat Mike Tyson to win the world heavyweight title in 1990?

27 Against which boxer did former world heavyweight champion Larry Holmes make a comeback at the age of 41?

28 Which world heavyweight boxing champion never actually won a world title fight?

29 What tragic fate befell world welterweight champion Benny Kid Paret in 1962 and world featherweight champion Davey Moore in 1963?

30 Which Labour MP said in 1991 "There's only one winner in professional boxing. I have never seen a promoter suffering from punch-drunkenness or brain damage."?

Cricket - Part 1
• QUESTIONS •

1 What did the great Dr W.G. Grace's initials stand for?

2 Which English county did Gary Sobers captain?

3 What is the full name of the famous "Gabba" ground in Brisbane?

4 When was the infamous "Bodyline" series played in Australia?

5 Who scored a century at Swansea in July 1991, in just 26 minutes?

6 Where would you be if you were watching cricket at the Gaddafi Stadium?

7 Which was the last county to win the Gillette Cup?

8 Against which team did Gary Sobers score his 365 not out at Kingston, Jamaica?

9 Who won the County Championship in 1977?

10 Name the 10 ways in which a batsman can be out?

11 The Currie Cup is contested where?

12 What was unusual about the hat-tricks achieved by Gloucestershire bowler Mike Proctor against Essex in 1972 and Yorkshire in 1979?

13 What is the highest single innings score by England?

14 How old was Mushtaq Mohammad when he made his Test debut for Pakistan v West Indies at Lahore in the 1958–59 series?

15 What shock defeat did Yorkshire suffer in the Benson and Hedges Cup in 1976?

16 How many times did Surrey win the County Championship in the 1950s?

17 In a Test match between Australia and the West Indies in December, 1960, at Brisbane, the two sides together scored a total number of 1,474 runs – which team got more?

18 When Jim Laker took his record 19 wickets in a single Test match, against Australia at Old Trafford in 1956, how many runs did he concede?

19 Who did Sri Lanka beat to gain their first Test victory?

20 How high, in inches, is a stump?

21 Who was the first man to take 300 Test wickets?

22 C.B. Fry was a great cricketer – what were his other two most notable sporting achievements?

23 Who became the first professional cricketer to captain England and in what year?

24 Who was the first black player to captain the West Indies?

25 Who took 710 minutes to score a total of 147 runs in two innings for England against Australia at Old Trafford in 1981?

26 When was the first Test match played at Lord's?

27 How many first class hundreds did Sir Jack Hobbs score in his career?

28 After the 1990–91 tour of Pakistan by New Zealand, about whom did Martin Crowe say "He is the best that I have faced – ever."?

29 What was the name of the first women's cricket club, formed in 1887?

30 In what year did there cease to be a distinction between "Gentlemen" and "Players?"

Olympics – Part 1
• QUESTIONS •

1 Who is responsible for reviving the Olympic Games in modern times?

2 Where were the 1908 London Games originally scheduled to take place?

3 What did the Soviet Union do in 1979 to cause the mass boycott of the 1980 Moscow Games?

4 How many times have the Olympics been held in the African continent?

5 In what five sports did Great Britain win gold at the 1988 Seoul Olympics?

6 Which disgraced athlete ironically said, "It's something they can't take away from you," when speaking about his quest for a gold medal?

7 Who, in Montreal 1976, became the youngest ever winner of an Olympic gold in gymnastics, aged just 14 years and 313 days?

8 In which year were electronic scoreboards first used in the Olympics?

9 Women fencers compete at only one discipline – which one?

10 What was unique about the 1936 Olympic basketball tournament?

11 Love blossomed in the Melbourne 1956 games between a male hammer thrower and a female discus thrower – why did their marriage the following year make international headlines?

12 At Seoul in 1988, Carl Lewis became the first male athlete to retain which two titles?

13 Up until and including Seoul 1988, how many golds had Great Britain won in the four men's throwing disciplines?

14 At which Games were athletes first tested for drugs?

15 Which two future World heavyweight boxing champions won the Olympic heavyweight golds in 1964 and 1968?

16 Who was the first member of the House of Lords to win an Olympic gold medal and what was his event?

17 At which Games was cricket an Olympic sport?

18 Seb Coe and Steve Ovett stole the headlines after the 800 metres final in Moscow 1980 ... which other British runner was also in the race?

19 What was Enriqueta Basilio the first woman to do at the 1968 Mexico games?

20 The USSR made its debut at which games?

21 Which two cities in the USA have hosted the Olympics?

22 What was the name of the horse that Princess Anne rode in the 1976 Montreal equestrian events?

23 What three weapons do men use in fencing?

24 How many golds did swimmer Matt Biondi win at the 1988 Seoul Games?

25 What was the name of the Finnish woman javelin thrower who split Tessa Sanderson and Fatima Whitbread in the 1984 Los Angeles games?

26 What was the time that Ben Johnson ran in the 100 metres final at Seoul 1988, before he was disqualified for steroid abuse?

27 Which two new sports were included in the 1992 Barcelona Games?

28 In the 1968 Mexico City Games, no less than seven men beat the previous Olympic record at which one event?

29 Why were the Olympic equestrian events held in a different hemisphere to the main Summer Games in 1956?

30 How did American theology student Forrest Smithson lodge his protest against Sunday competition while winning gold in the 110 metres hurdles at the London Games in 1908?

Football World Cup – Part 1
• QUESTIONS •

1 When did Britain first get World Cup television coverage in colour?

2 Name England's five penalty takers in the dramatic 1990 semi-final against West Germany?

3 Scotland qualified for the 1986 World Cup Finals with a 2–0 aggregate play-off win against whom?

4 Who played on in a 1970 semi-final after breaking his collar bone?

5 Why were the 1958 finals a general success for the United Kingdom?

6 Holland have lost both their appearances in the World Cup Final – which other country has suffered the same misfortune?

7 Why was the kick-off between France and Hungary in the 1978 finals delayed for an hour?

8 Pat Jennings made his last international appearance in the 1986 finals against whom?

9 Italy suffered an embarrassing defeat at the hands of which emerging country in the 1966 finals?

10 Who was the leading scorer in the Finals of the 1978 tournament?

11 Name the dog who recovered the stolen Jules Rimet Trophy before the 1966 finals?

12 Hungary is the only country to have scored 10 goals in a single match during the finals of a World Cup, against whom?

13 In the 1982 World Cup Finals, France conceded a goal after just 27 seconds of their match against which country?

14 How many different countries have won the World Cup?

15 Who scored the only goal of the 1990 World Cup final?

16 Who beat Romania, Colombia and Argentina en route to a quarter final spot in the 1990 tournament?

17 What country reached the 1986 finals without staging a single qualifying match at home?

18 Who finished third in the 1974 finals after beating Brazil in a play-off?

19 Which was the last host nation to win the World Cup?

20 Why were Mexico banned from the 1990 qualifiers?

21 Name the first black African nation to qualify for the finals.

22 Which nation produced the shock of the 1982 finals with a 2–1 group win over West Germany?

23 Which player holds the record for the most goals scored in a single tournament Finals?

24 Which country will never be able to improve on its formidable World Cup record of three wins and three runners-up spots?

25 Who was the last goalkeeper to captain a World Cup winning team?

26 How old was Norman Whiteside when he made his first appearance in the 1982 finals?

27 What was unusual about a World Cup qualifying match between Chile and the USSR in 1973?

28 In the 1986 finals, which country did Notts County's Rachid Harkouk play for?

29 Why was there no actual World Cup Final in the 1950 tournament?

30 Why was Tunisian Ali Ben Maceur instrumental in England's exit from the 1986 finals?

Superstars - Part 1

• QUESTIONS •

1 Who did Ginger McCain train to a place in sporting folklore?

2 What is the world record fee for a rugby league player . . . and who was it paid for?

3 Which NHL ice hockey superstar said about himself: "I'm lucky, I'm God-gifted and I am the first to admit it"?

4 For what was El Cordobes a hero in Spain?

5 Which USA jockey holds the world record for the 598 winners he rode in one season in 1989?

6 At which Olympic games did Nadia Comaneci collect her unprecedented seven perfect 10.00 scores in gymnastics?

7 Which thrilling French rugby player turned his back on the international scene for the last time after the World Cup quarter finals in 1991?

8 Which snooker legend won the Formula One World Professional Championships 15 times in a row?

9 Nigel Mansell won the first five Formula One Grand Prix of the 1992 season. At which circuit did he do it?

10 Which motor racing legend won the World Drivers' Championships five times in the 1950s?

11 How many gold medals did Mark Spitz collect in the 1972 Munich Olympics?

12 Which cricketing hero made his final appearance in Test cricket in 1974, at Trinidad?

13 At which five weights did the great Sugar Ray Leonard win world titles?

14 In May 1992, Inter Milan agreed to pay £9.2 million for which football star?

15 Apart from his success as a pop superstar, Julio Iglesias has another claim to fame . . . he played in goal for which great Spanish football team?

16 Which golfer said: "I smoke, I drink, I like a bit of fun. I want to be the best, but I'll do it in my own little way"?

17 Which outspoken tennis player once said of himself: "Really, I'm very shy and quiet."?

18 With which skipper do you associate the USA's modern success in the America's Cup?

19 Which tennis prodigy won four grand slam titles before she was 18 years old?

20 Who became the most expensive British footballer after the Paul Gascoine-Lazio deal was put on ice after his FA Cup final injury?

21 Between 1978 and 1990, Martina Navratilova appeared in an incredible 11 out of a possible 13 women's singles finals at Wimbledon . . . which two years did she miss?

22 Which rock megastar used to own Watford Football Club?

23 Who once said about his golfing style: "I've got a bad swing, a bad stance and a bad grip. But my bank manager loves me."?

24 Which American footballer took up a career in heavy-weight boxing after leaving the New York Jets?

25 Which Italian soccer superstar was transferred from Fiorentina to Juventus for £7.7 million in 1990?

26 Which living squash legend won his 10th consecutive British Open Championships in 1991?

27 Bjorn Borg became the first tennis player of modern times to win the Wimbledon men's singles five times in a row . . . although this feat had been performed before, what advantage did Borg's predecessors have that he did not?

28 Which Hollywood box office star owns the Tampa Bay Bandits American football team?

29 Which Australian cricket captain said about Ian Botham: "I know we can beat England, but we just can't cope with Botham. He's a one man army."?

30 Which international film star was given locker number 007, when he joined the exclusive Lake Sherwood Golf Club in Los Angeles?

General - Part 2

• QUESTIONS •

1 In which month is the Derby held?

2 What body oversees the sport of polo?

3 Which two adversaries attracted the highest attendance at Arsenal's Highbury Stadium in 1966?

4 What sport do the Stentofon Worthing Bears play?

5 Baseball's World Series is won by the first side to win how many games?

6 What is the oche?

7 What are the Oxford Torpids and the Cambridge Lents?

8 What is Jai Alai?

9 During which race at Royal Ascot in 1989, were the "sonic" binoculars used to unseat jockey Greville Starkey from Ile de Chypre?

10 What are hippodromes?

11 Hampshire County cricket club played some of their home matches in which other county?

12 What piece of netball history did Welshman Colin King create in March 1992?

13 What are the four individual disciplines in women's gymnastics?

14 With which sport do you associate the Milk Race?

15 Where is the 1996 British Open golf championship to be held?

16 In the 1980s and early 1990s, the two dominant players in world squash were both called Khan ... what are their first names?

17 What is the grand champion of Sumo wrestling called?

18 In 1991, which country broke the USA's exclusive 34 year hold on the world team water-skiing championships?

19 What piece of cricket history did Indian batsman Sachin Tendulkar create in April 1992?

20 Why was the winner of the 1992 Grand National so aptly named?

21 What is Pop Warner football?

22 What was the name of the yacht which won the Whitbread round the world yacht race in 1990?

23 Essendon, Carlton, Hawthorn and Footscray are household names for followers of which sport?

24 During the late 1950s and early 1960s, which important race was regularly held at Aintree ... other than the Grand National?

25 What are a cleek, a spoon and a brassie?

26 What piece of football World Cup history will be made at the Detroit Silverdome in the 1994 USA tournament?

27 What are the three main international cycling tours?

28 What did Great Britain's Lisa Opie win in 1991, which had not been won by a Briton since 1961?

29 What sensation did Italian swimmer Ilaria Tocchini cause at her country's national championships in 1991?

30 What first did Boris Mavla achieve when he rowed in the winning Oxford eight at the 1992 boat race?

Football - Part 2

• QUESTIONS •

1 What piece of football history did Wendy Toms achieve in the 1991–92 season?

2 What England football hero had a Number Three chart hit with "Head Over Heels in Love."?

3 How high is a football goal?

4 Which stadium did Queens Park Rangers move to in 1962, only to move back to Loftus Road the following year?

5 Which Merseyside clubs did the great Dixie Dean play for?

6 Which was the first country to beat England at Wembley and in what year?

7 Where was the 1992 African Nations Cup staged?

8 Which was the last club to win the FA Cup in successive years before Tottenham in 1981 and 1982?

9 Which is the only club in England and Scottish League football with a J in its name?

10 Who made Trevor Francis the first £1 million footballer in Britain by buying him from Birmingham City?

11 Which was the only football league club to be managed by a doctor in the 1990–91 season?

12 What is the connection between Peter Shilton and Terry Paine, the two players who have made the most league appearances?

13 Who were the four 1992 FA Cup semi-finalists?

14 Alberto Tarantini was the third member of the 1978 World Cup winning Argentina side to sign for a British club – which one?

15 Which club scored an incredible total of 10 goals in its only two appearances in the FA Cup final?

16 Igor Belanov scored a hat-trick for the USSR in one of their 1986 World Cup finals matches, but they still ended up losing – to which side?

17 Who scored the goal which sensationally dumped Arsenal out of the 1991–92 FA Cup competition?

18 Who was the first manager ever to be sacked by Southampton?

19 Which Rugby League side do Leeds United share their ground with?

20 What has the World Club Championship been known as since 1980?

21 Who was the 1991 Football Writers' Player of the Year?

22 Which side scored the most goals in Division One in 1938 . . . but still got relegated?

23 Name the four England players with 100 or more caps.

24 Against which country did Bobby Charlton score his 49th – and last – goal for England?

25 Which tycoon tried to merge several Israeli clubs into Jerusalem United in 1990?

26 Name the six London clubs that have signed Clive Allen.

27 Who was Bill Shankly talking about when he said: "He had the opposition so worried, they would have a man marking him when they were warming up before the kick off"?

28 What do the initials FIFA stand for?

29 French superstar Eric Cantona scored his first English football league goal for Leeds against which club in 1992?

30 Who was the first player to be dropped from England's 1966 World Cup winning team . . . and who replaced him?

Rugby League
• QUESTIONS •

1 Who was the 1991 Division One Player of the Year?

2 What was the Regal Trophy formerly known as?

3 Who or what are the Kumuls?

4 Which club has won the Yorkshire Cup most times?

5 When was the last time Great Britain won a home series against Australia?

6 In 1992, Andy Gregory marked his eighth appearance in the Challenge Cup Final with a winner's medal – how many times before that had he been a losing finalist?

7 What record did Wigan set in their 1992 Challenge Cup semi-final?

8 What was the final score in Great Britain's historic First Test victory over Australia at Wembley in October 1990?

9 In what year was the law introduced that reduced Rugby League teams to 13 players from the original 15?

10 What nickname was given to New Zealand's first ever Rugby League touring side by their Union counterparts, who were scornful about the advent of professionalism?

11 Runcorn Highfield drew a match with Carlisle in late 1991 to end an extended run of how many consecutive defeats?

12 When, at last, did Widnes finally win the League Championship?

13 Which club was Ellery Hanley playing for when he was "Man of Steel" in 1985?

14 How many tries did Martin Offiah score in the two tests between France and Great Britain in early 1991?

15 Rugby League is the most popular sport in which two Australian states?

16 What do the French call Rugby League?

17 For which Rugby Union clubs did record-breaking winger Martin Offiah play before switching codes?

18 When was the Rugby League World Cup first staged and when did it cease to be played in its original format?

19 Which Widnes and St Helens legend was known as the Wild Bull of the Pampas?

20 Kent Invicta joined the Rugby League in 1983 – what were they called when they left two years later?

21 When was Rugby League's International Board founded?

22 Whose record of captaining Great Britain 17 times did Ellery Hanley beat in the Test against France at Perpignan in January 1991?

23 Which country was granted full International Board status in 1978?

24 Who was banned after becoming the first ever Rugby League player to fail a drugs test, only to have the suspension quashed after it was revealed that his drink had been spiked?

25 Who, aged 41 years and 29 days, is the oldest winner of a Challenge Cup medal?

26 What award is presented to the Man of the Match in the Premiership final?

27 Which amateur side hit the headlines in 1978 by knocking Halifax, a professional club, out of the John Player Cup?

28 Name the trophy which could only be won by Australia or New Zealand?

29 Who made 239 consecutive appearances for Widnes between 1977 and 1982?

30 Name the lone club which voted AGAINST resigning from the Rugby Union at the historic meeting which gave birth to Rugby League in 1895?

Horse Racing

• QUESTIONS •

1 How many times did Red Rum compete in the Grand National?

2 Which English monarch founded Ascot racecourse?

3 Over what distance is the Oaks run?

4 What was the name of the first winner ridden by Princess Anne, at Redcar in 1986?

5 What was unusual about the 1957 Grand National?

6 Who were the first five jockeys to ride 3,000 winners in Britain?

7 Which is the oldest English Classic and when was it first run?

8 In what year did Geraldine Rees become the first woman to complete the Grand National?

9 What is the premium prize in Australian horse racing?

10 Who owned the legendary Arkle?

11 At which course was the Derby run during World War II?

12 What amazing geographical and racing feat did jockey Paul Cook perform in 1981?

13 At which courses are the five English Classics run?

14 Which horse was the first ever Derby winner and in what year?

15 In which year did Sir Gordon Richards ride his record 269 winners?

16 Where would you find Les Lands racecourse?

17 Which was the stallion that sired Shergar?

18 Before Red Rum, which was the last horse to win the Grand National in consecutive years?

19 Name the only horse to beat Brigadier Gerard.

20 At which racecourse did an ambulanceman and a jockey both die on Boxing Day 1991?

21 Which trainer and which owner were both the first to break the £1 million barrier in prize money, in 1985?

22 Which three races make up the US Triple Crown?

23 About which Derby flop did trainer Andre Chabre say: "He was a false favourite at Epsom. Some people said he didn't go downhill, but he didn't go uphill either."?

24 What is the French equivalent of the Derby?

25 What was ironic about Seagram's 1991 Grand National victory?

26 Which Derby did Lester Pigott win in 1991?

27 Who was the only rider to break the stranglehold that Peter Scudamore and John Francome had on the National Hunt Jockey title in the 1980's – and in what year?

28 Which horse was eventually awarded the 1989 Oaks in 1990 after the Jockey Club finally disqualified the Aga Khan's Aliysa?

29 Which successful flat trainer publicly backed himself to train one hundred two-year-old winners in the 1992 season?

30 The longest-priced winner of a horse race in the world was Anntelle in the 1982 Norman Ross Handicap in Sydney – what were the odds?

Athletics - Part 2
• QUESTIONS •

1 Which Scottish-born England resident won two Commonwealth golds in 1986 . . . for Wales?

2 In the USA, how is notification given of the last lap?

3 Carl Lewis set a new World Record for the 100 metres in the 1991 Tokyo World Championships . . . name the other two USA medallists.

4 Name the venue of the first athletics World Championships.

5 Who was the 1983 women's 400 metres and 800 metres World champion?

6 Which country dominated the men's cross country championships between 1986 and 1992?

7 In what year were the AAA and the WAAA abolished?

8 When did Ben Johnson make a comeback to international athletics after his two year ban for drug taking?

9 Who is the only woman to have won Olympic gold medals in the 100 metres, 200 metres and 400 metres?

10 Name Ireland's 1983 5,000 metres world champion.

11 Which American middle distance runner is British athlete Richard Slaney married to?

12 Name the events in a heptathlon.

13 In which years did Steve Cram win the European 1,500 metres title?

14 Which two women broke the marathon record within three days of each other?

15 In which country did Britain's Steve Backley set a world record with a javelin throw of 91.46 m, in January 1992?

16 Name the versatile Moroccan middle and long distance runner who, at the end of 1991, held world records in four different events.

17 How many world records were set in women's athletics in 1991?

18 Which triple jumper first used to encourage the crowd to clap in time in order to spur him on for his event?

19 Who was the patron of the AAA?

20 In which event has France had three different world record holders since 1980?

21 In which year did the USA first win the Olympic women's long jump?

22 In which event was China's Huang Zhihong world champion in 1991?

23 How old was the oldest recorded finisher of a marathon?

24 In which year was the women's 10,000 metres event introduced to the Olympics?

25 Which British girl has won nine WAAA indoor shot put titles?

26 Which Briton won gold in the 100 metres at the Moscow Olympics?

27 How many lanes are there usually on an international athletics track?

28 Who won the women's javelin gold in the 1984 Los Angeles Olympics?

29 Which female athlete won her first marathon attempt, in 1991, recording the fastest ever debut time?

30 What important 1927 invention changed the face of sprinting?

Snooker

• QUESTIONS •

1 Which two players contested the Strachan Professional Championship final in 1992?

2 What is the relationship between snooker greats Joe, Fred and Steve Davis?

3 How many consecutive shots are needed for a total clearance?

4 Who was the first person, other than Joe Davis, to win the World Professional Championship and in what year?

5 What were snooker balls originally made from?

6 In what sport did snooker's Eddie Charlton win a 1950 Australian Championship?

7 What is the closest Jimmy White has come to winning the World Championship?

8 Seven Englishmen were in the 1991 World Rankings top ten . . . name the three non-Englishmen.

9 The World Championships were staged outside Britain for the first and only time in 1975. Where were they held?

10 Which two women contested the 1991 Trusthouse Forte Ladies World Championship final?

11 Which colour spot is nearest to the top cushion?

12 Who holds the record for the fastest 100, in two minutes and 45 seconds?

13 In which year was the Pot Black tournament temporarily discontinued?

14 Who was the first non-British snooker player to win the Embassy World Professional Championship?

15 How much did Joe Davis receive in prize money when he won the first World Championships in 1927?

16 What break is possible when only the colours remain on the table?

17 Which player sought psychiatric help in a bid to overcome his fear of using a rest?

18 What is the minimum length of a snooker cue?

19 On his way to victory in the 1977 Benson and Hedges Masters, Doug Mountjoy overcame three former World Champions. Who were they?

20 Who was the first player to win the World Title using a two-piece cue?

21 Who scored the first officially recognized maximum break?

22 Who won the World Professional title at his first attempt in 1972?

23 Which great retired from the game aged 58 years, after being ranked 126 in the world in 1991?

24 Before Stormseal, who were the two previous sponsors of the UK Open championships?

25 What is the diameter of a snooker ball?

26 What is the connection between Tony Meo, Jimmy White and Jack the Ripper?

27 Who won the only BCE Canadian Masters?

28 Who was Steve Davis playing when he recorded the first ever televised 147 break?

29 Which current professional was the World Amateur champion in 1988?

30 1990 World Champion Stephen Hendry was knocked out of the 1991 World Championship by which player?

Hockey

• QUESTIONS •

1 In what year was the first hockey World Cup?

2 What is the maximum circumference of a hockey ball?

3 Which British team was one of the sides to play in the first ever Olympic hockey match at the 1900 Paris Games?

4 Where is the first British National Hockey Stadium to be built?

5 How many goals did Great Britain concede in coming bottom of the 1990 Champions Trophy?

6 Where was the first hockey club founded?

7 Who were the four semi-finalists in the 1992 Hockey Association Cup?

8 When was the Hockey Association founded?

9 Which was the only match that Great Britain lost on the way to gold in the 1988 Seoul Olympics?

10 How wide is a hockey goal?

11 Which England and Great Britain goalkeeper of the 1950s was also an accomplished sprinter, who narrowly missed being selected to run in the 1948 London Olympics?

12 Great Britain's hockey team was not originally invited to play in the 1984 Los Angeles Olympics – how did they end up with the bronze medal?

13 With which country do you associate the great Ties Kruize?

14 Which 1986 hockey match was watched by more than six million people on British television?

15 When was a hockey match first played on an artificial surface?

16 Who scored England's dramatic last minute equalizer and then the extra-time winner in the 1986 World Cup semi-final against West Germany?

17 Which country has won the World Cup most times?

18 Which Scottish club lost against HGC Wassenaar in the 1991 European Champions Cup final?

19 Against which country did Sean Kerly celebrate his 100th outdoor international cap with his 50th international goal?

20 Which country won Olympic gold the first time it entered a team for the games, in 1928, without conceding a goal in any of its matches?

21 The women's Great Britain team's 2–1 victory over Australia in March 1992 was their first win over Australia since which year?

22 What small piece of hockey history did Slough and St Alban's make when they met on January 19, 1992, for a national league match?

23 What accolade was Great Britain's Ian Taylor awarded in his first World Cup tournament in 1978?

24 In which city was the 1982 World Cup played?

25 Which side lost 24–1 to India in the 1932 Los Angeles Olympics?

26 In 1985, a men's club from Spain won the European Champions Cup for the first time – what was the club?

27 What was the name of the Australian great of the 1970s and 80s, who was also an opening batsman for Western Australia, a doctor and an Australian Member of Parliament?

28 Name the two Great Britain substitutes brought on in the dying seconds of the 1988 Seoul Olympics final to ensure they also got gold medals.

29 Which First Division football club wanted to sign Sean Kerly as a schoolboy?

30 What link is there between the Hockey Association and Jack the Ripper?

Tennis
• QUESTIONS •

1 What is the name of John McEnroe's tennis-playing younger brother?

2 The horrible weather caused what first at the 1991 Wimbledon Championships?

3 Who did Boris Becker beat to win his first Wimbledon?

4 How many service games did Stefan Edberg drop when losing to Michael Stich in the 1991 Wimbledon semi-finals?

5 Bunny Austin was the last British men's singles finalist at Wimbledon, in 1938 . . . how many games did he win in his three set defeat by Don Budge?

6 What was Billie Jean King's maiden name?

7 When was the last time that both the men's singles finalists at Wimbledon were left-handed?

8 Where are the Australian Open Championships played?

9 What were the two Grand Slam singles titles won by Virginia Wade?

10 How did former British number one tennis star Annabel Croft make sure she always got to the ball in late 1991 and early 1992?

11 What size and weight restrictions are there on a tennis racquet?

12 Who is the Davis Cup named after?

13 Who partnered John Lloyd to Wimbledon mixed doubles titles in 1983 and 1984?

14 Which Grand Slam title did Britain's Sue Barker win?

15 Which French tennis player has released a reggae album?

16 How many times did Bjorn Borg win the French Open Championships?

17 Who did Monica Seles beat to win her first Australian Open?

18 Who wrecked Boris Becker's hopes of a third consecutive Wimbledon title in 1987?

19 Name the first three women to do the Grand Slam.

20 What was unusual about Monica Seles' win against Gabriela Sabatini in the 1991 Virginia Slims Championship final in New York?

21 Which Grand Slam tournament evaded both Arthur Ashe and John Newcombe?

22 When was the last all British Wimbledon singles final?

23 Whose record of 157 tournament wins was beaten by Martina Navratilova in February 1992?

24 What was banned by the ITF in 1981, after making a controversial entrance into the tennis market in 1977?

25 Which country knocked holders France out of the Davis Cup at the quarter final stage in 1992?

26 Against whom did John Lloyd lose his 1977 final in the Australian Open?

27 Name the four players who lost to Bjorn Borg in Wimbledon men's singles finals.

28 In what year did Martina Navratilova win her first Grand Slam title as a citizen of the USA?

29 Players under 18 years old won three Grand Slam titles in the 1980s . . . who were they?

30 How many aces did Boris Becker serve in the entire 1991 Wimbledon Championships?

Cricket – Part 2

• QUESTIONS •

1 Where was the first ever Test match played?

2 Who was the first person to score a test triple century?

3 Which Test umpire hops superstitiously whenever a batsman's or a team score is made up of the same three figures?

4 Which current Indian bowler took 16 wickets in his first test?

5 Which is the only first class county not to win or come second in the County Championship?

6 Which country suffered an embarrassing first class defeat at the hands of Oxford University in May, 1992?

7 Which Scottish international goalkeeper has played cricket for Scotland?

8 Who was the last knight to play in a test match?

9 Ted Dexter is the current chairman of selectors, who was his predecessor?

10 At which ground in England (other than Lord's) would you find the Grace Gates?

11 Which bowler was not selected for the 1990 New Zealand touring party but ended up playing in a game when he turned up to watch?

12 Who is the first player to take 4,000 wickets in a first class career?

13 Which bowler was nicknamed "Deadly"?

14 Who was bowling when Gary Sobers hit his 36 runs off one over?

15 Which England cricketer appeared at Test level in four different decades?

16 Where do Oxford and Cambridge Universities play their home games?

17 The highest first class score is 499 by Hanif Mohammed. How was he out?

18 Who is the only batsman to average more than 100 in an English season twice?

19 Which was the first county to win the Nat West Trophy and Benson and Hedges Cup in the same year?

20 Who was the first Sri Lankan to score a Test 200?

21 Which Test country was skittled all out for 26 against England in 1955?

22 How many runs did Don Bradman need to score in his last Test innings to have a career Test average of 100 . . . and how many did he get?

23 Which four sets of brothers have played Test cricket for New Zealand?

24 When did the laws first permit bowlers to deliver the ball overarm?

25 In New Zealand, 77 runs were taken off one over of only five official balls (due to the umpire's error) in 1990. Who was the bowler?

26 Who won the 1990 Norse Hydro Village Championship?

27 Who hit the headlines in 1980 for using a metal bat?

28 In 1991, which Gloucestershire player took his first-ever first class wicket against the touring West Indian team?

29 Which three England captains failed to win a Test match in the 1980s?

30 Who, in 1991, became the first batsman to score a century against every first class county, including his own?

Olympics - Part 2
• QUESTIONS •

1 The first ever Olympic swimming dead heat occurred at the 1984 Los Angeles games in the women's 100 metres freestyle . . . name the swimmers.

2 In Helsinki 1952, Emil Zatopek and Dana Zatopkova became the first ever husband and wife to win golds in track and field events at the same games. Which country did they come from?

3 Who coached Olga Korbut to gold at the Munich 1972 Olympics?

4 Ann Packer stunned everyone by winning gold at Tokyo in 1964 at a distance she had only ever run twice before the games. What was the race?

5 What are the two types of wrestling contested in the Olympics?

6 Which is the only country to have entered a team in every modern Olympic games?

7 In which year was the International Olympic Committee founded?

8 How old was Swedish shooter Oscar Swahn when he won a medal in the 1920 Antwerp games?

9 Why was there an Olympiad in 1906, two years after the St Louis games and two years before the London Olympics?

10 In which year did Great Britain top the gold medal table, with 57?

11 Allan Wells' victory in the 100 metres at Moscow 1980 was the slowest Olympic title winning time for the event since which games?

12 Boris Onischenko earned infamy for his efforts to cheat to Olympic gold in which sport at the 1976 Montreal games?

13 Where were the first Olympic games of modern times held in 1896?

14 A mystery boy, aged no more than 10 years old, won gold at the 1900 Paris Olympics when he was called in at the last minute to cox the Dutch coxed pairs rowers . . . what nationality was he?

15 Who was the first ever women's heptathlon Olympic champion?

16 At which games was the Olympic flame first used?

17 USA's Edward Eagan was the first man ever to win gold medals at both the Winter (1932) and Summer (1920) Olympics . . . what were his two events?

18 How many times have the summer Olympics been held in the southern hemisphere?

19 At which Olympics was the women's marathon run for the first time?

20 How many members of the ill-fated Israeli Olympic team were murdered in the notorious attack by Arabs in the 1972 Munich games?

21 Who is the only man to win the 5,000 metres, 10,000 metres and the marathon at the same games?

22 What nationality was Paavo Nurmi, the runner barred from the 1932 Los Angeles games on accusations of professionalism?

23 In what event was Great Britain's only gold of the 1952 Helsinki Olympics?

24 At the 1984 Los Angeles games, USA's Valerie Briscoe-Hooks became the first athlete to complete which Olympic double?

25 Which East German athlete split Seb Coe and Steve Ovett in the Moscow 1980 games 1,500 metres final?

26 Why was the 3,000 metres steeplechase of the 1932 Los Angeles games not 3,000 metres long?

27 What was the only track and field world record to be broken in the 1984 Los Angeles games?

28 What 100 metres and 200 metres Olympic firsts were both achieved at the 1968 Mexico City games?

29 Why did Olmeus Charles have the track in the Olympic stadium to himself for eight minutes at the 1976 Montreal games?

30 Between 1912 and 1948, Olympic medals were awarded for artistic achievement in five categories – what were they?

Football World Cup – Part 2
• QUESTIONS •

1 Who uttered the immortal words . . . "Some people are on the pitch, they think it's all over – it is now!" at the end of the 1966 final?

2 Which country was beaten in its only appearance in a World Cup Final?

3 Who sang the England team's 1990 official World Cup song?

4 Argentina lost one group game on their way to winning the 1978 World Cup. Who beat them and by what score?

5 Two nations have lost successive World Cup finals – who were they?

6 Apart from England, which is the only country to win every World Cup Final in which it has played?

7 Who took over as England skipper after Bryan Robson was injured in the 1986 tournament?

8 What unfortunate precedent did Italy's Antonio Cabrini set in the 1982 World Cup Final?

9 Which nation was originally selected to host the 1986 finals, which were eventually played in Mexico?

10 How many countries have won the World Cup just once?

11 Jack Charlton's Republic of Ireland reached the last eight in the 1992 tournament without doing what?

12 When did Wales last qualify for the finals?

13 In which city was the first ever World Cup final played?

14 England's Ray Wilkins was sent off during the 1986 finals in a group match against which country?

15 Only two players have scored at every stage of a finals tournament. One was France's Just Fontaine . . . who was the other?

16 Which English referee awarded two penalties in the 1974 final?

17 Northern Ireland's glorious campaign of the 1982 finals was crowned by a 1–0 victory over the hosts, Spain? Who scored the goal?

18 Which nation inflicted a shock defeat on England in the 1950 finals?

19 Scotland have only won four of their matches in their various campaigns in the finals. Which countries were their victims?

20 In which two of Brazil's World Cup winning teams did the great Pele play?

21 Who celebrated the end of a two year suspension by finishing top scorer in the 1982 World Cup finals?

22 Two host nations have lost a World Cup final. Who were they?

23 Scotland have played in all five of the World Cup finals tournaments between 1974 and 1990, but under five different managers. Can you name them?

24 What is the record attendance for a World Cup match?

25 Extra time has been required to settle a World Cup final three times – in which years?

26 Which have won the most World Cup finals – teams from South America or teams from Europe?

27 Gary Lineker scored six of England's seven goals in the 1986 finals. Who scored the other and against which country?

28 Why did the Northern Ireland Football Association order the national side NOT to play two out of three group matches in the 1958 finals?

29 Why did India withdraw from the 1950 finals, the only time they have managed to qualify?

30 Name all the players in the victorious 1966 England World Cup final side.

Winter Sports

• QUESTIONS •

1 Between 1985 and 1991, which country held the European and world ice dancing titles?

2 Who was Britain's most infamous entrant to the 1988 Calgary Winter Olympics?

3 Who was Austria's double gold medallist in the 1991 ski-ing World Championships?

4 What are the names of cross-country ski-ing and downhill ski-ing?

5 Where is the Cresta Run?

6 Name the four different Alpine ski-ing events?

7 Who is the female ice skater who has been world figure skating champion four times and held the European title six times?

8 How many winter golds have Great Britain won since the inauguration of the Winter Olympics in 1924?

9 What is the minimum length of a bobsleigh course?

10 From its introduction in 1968 to the 1988 winter games, which country dominated the biathlon event?

11 Who won the women's European figure skating championship for France in 1991?

12 Who won gold for Great Britain in the two man bobsleigh in 1964?

13 Who won Olympic gold in the 90 metres ski jump in the 1992 winter games at Albertville?

14 What are the first names of Great Britain's ski-ing Bell brothers?

15 In British hockey, where would you find the Bees and the Wasps?

16 Which event is nicknamed the "Super G"?

17 Where and when did Great Britain shock the world by winning the Olympic ice hockey gold medal?

18 What was the first form of ski-ing introduced in the Olympics?

19 Which film star dominated the world figure skating championships between 1927 and 1936?

20 Until 1988, only four countries had won the Olympic ice hockey gold . . . name them.

21 In which year was the Super Giant Slalom first included in the Winter Olympics?

22 What are the targets called in curling?

23 Which world giant slalom champion was killed in a car crash in 1991?

24 Who swept the board with a hat-trick of gold medals in the 1968 Olympics Alpine ski-ing events?

25 In which two consecutive Olympic games did John Curry and Robin Cousins win figure skating gold medals . . . the only time that Great Britain has retained a winter Olympic title?

26 In which country were the British Bobsleigh Championships held in 1992?

27 The Albertville winter Olympics of 1992 had speed ski-ing as an exhibition sport . . . in what tragic circumstances did a competitor die during the games?

28 How was the Olympic bobsleigh event altered in 1932?

29 Which two events make up the Olympic biathlon?

30 What was unusual about the Canadian teams in the early Olympic ice hockey tournaments?

American Football

• QUESTIONS •

1 To the nearest $10,000, what were the average earnings of a National Football League player in 1991?

2 Where was Superbowl XXVI played?

3 Which teams play at Soldier Field and The Superdome?

4 Which team won the first ever Superbowl, in 1967?

5 Only once has the Rose Bowl not been played at the Rose Bowl in Pasedena . . . in which year?

6 At which famous stadium do Gridiron teams from the USA meet to contest the American Bowl?

7 Why were the Los Angeles Raiders' silver and black colours banned from schools in Denver?

8 Which two teams share the NFL record of 18 consecutive wins?

9 Who missed the field goal in the dying seconds of Superbowl XXV to leave New York Giants as winners by just one point?

10 Who was the NFL player of the year in 1990?

11 Shaver tycoon Victor Kiam used to own which American Conference team?

12 How many NFL/NFC championships did Green Bay Packers win in the 1960s, as well as two Superbowls?

13 Who coached the London Monarchs to victory in the first ever World Bowl?

14 Which was the only Wild Card team to win Superbowl in the 1980s?

15 Where is the Pro Bowl played?

16 On May 12, 1991, which Gridiron team registered 14 sacks, beating the old Pro football record of 12 in a game?

17 How many rounds are there in the NFL college draft?

18 What are the London Monarchs cheerleaders called?

19 In the 1990 season, Tennessee beat Virginia 23–22 to win what?

20 Which team has lost in each of its four appearances in Superbowl?

21 What do the Bears, the Cardinals and the Staleys have in common?

22 There were two NFL player strikes in the 1980s, in which years did they happen?

23 What is a "Hail Mary"?

24 What ignominy did Baltimore Colts suffer in 1982?

25 Which stadium is nick-named "The House of Pain"?

26 What is the highest number of points scored by one team in a single quarter in Superbowl history?

27 Who were the 1983 European Champions at American Football?

28 Name the three European-based teams, who played in the inaugural season of the World League of American Football?

29 Where is the Joe Robbie stadium?

30 Complete the names of the two following teams, which enjoyed brief NFL success in the 1920s. Frankford . . . and Providence. . . .?

Golf

• QUESTIONS •

1 Who was the skipper of the successful USA Ryder Cup team of 1991?

2 Which golf club did Sandy Lyle present to Augusta National after his famous bunker shot which clinched the 1988 US Masters?

3 What was Ian Woosnam's first major win?

4 Why was John Daly's victory in the 1991 US PGA so extraordinary?

5 What distinction does the Tuctu Course in Peru hold?

6 What should the British Open trophy be used for?

7 In which year did Tony Jacklin win his only US Open title?

8 Who was Bernhard Langer's opponent in the dramatic final round of the 1991 Ryder Cup?

9 Who was the last person to win successive US Masters titles before Nick Faldo?

10 Which famous course did golfing great Ben Hogan never play?

11 At which course were the first 12 British Open championships played?

12 Why did Jose Maria Olazabal stage a sit-down protest at the Mediterranean Open in March 1991?

13 What was notable about Bobby Jones' victories in both the British and US Opens of 1930?

14 Who missed the agonisingly short putt on the 18th at St Andrews in 1970 to let Jack Nicklaus scoop his second British Open?

15 Who was caddy to Nick Faldo when he lifted the British Open in 1990?

16 How many feathers were needed to make a "Feathery" golf ball?

17 Who won the British Open in 1868, the year after Tom Morris Senior won it for the last time?

18 Who sponsors Payne Stewart's colourful attire when he competes in tournament golf?

19 Ryder Cup captain Bernard Gallagher is the club pro at which course?

20 In the play-off round for the 1991 US Open, what was Payne Stewart's winning score?

21 What was Japanese golfer Isao Aoki's notable achievement in the 1980 British Open at Muirfield?

22 Who won the 1991 women's US Open title?

23 What was different about the 1958 US PGA championships?

24 Who scored successive holes-in-one at the 1977 Martini International?

25 Which course did Ian Woosnam describe as "like something from Mars" in 1991?

26 What did Swedish golfer Johan Tumba allegedly do in 1991 that required the attentions of Scotland Yard forensic experts?

27 Who is the youngest player to have participated in a US PGA event, at the age of 16 years and two months?

28 Who scored the most birdies in the 1991 British Open, with 19?

29 How much did Phil Mickelson win for his victory in the Tucson Open on the 1991 American tour?

30 Who has played in the most Ryder Cup matches with eight appearances spanning 16 years?

Football – Part 3

• QUESTIONS •

1 When was the Football Association founded?

2 Which was the only side to beat Arsenal in the 1990–91 season?

3 Who are the five English clubs to have won the League and F.A. Cup double?

4 Which football league club has Test cricketer Ian Botham played for?

5 Where is the headquarters of the Football Association?

6 What is the South American football championship known as?

7 How many times was Kenny Dalglish capped by Scotland?

8 Which Division One side drew more than half their League games in the 1978–79 season?

9 In which country does the club Flamurtari Viora play?

10 Arsenal have avoided relegation from Division One longer than any other club . . . when was the last time they were not in the top flight?

11 An FA Cup final replay was not held at Wembley in 1970, when Chelsea and Leeds met at which venue?

12 How many goals did Pele score for Brazil?

13 What international tournament was held at Meadowbank Thistle's ground in 1986?

14 Which club sold Dutch star Ruud Gullit to AC Milan for £5.5 million in 1987?

15 Which teams did Robert Maxwell want to merge to form the Thames Valley Royals?

16 Who scored five goals for England against Cyprus in 1975?

17 In which year did Liverpool win the European Super Cup for the first time?

18 Who were the two Argentinians bought by Tottenham after the 1978 World Cup finals?

19 Which Prime Minister claimed to know more about football than politics?

20 What was the name of the Top 10 hit released by Tottenham stars Chris Waddle and Glenn Hoddle in 1987?

21 Which was the first club to win the European Cup, the European Cup Winners Cup, the UEFA Cup and the European Super Cup?

22 Who won the 1992 African Nations Cup?

23 Who were the two sponsors of the English football league prior to Barclays?

24 Who scored on his debut for England against France in February 1992?

25 Which club won the German Bundesliga Championship in 1992?

26 What was stolen in 1895, never to be seen again?

27 At which World Cup were substitutes first allowed?

28 Which have won more World Club Championships – European or South American sides?

29 An international tournament was played at Queens Park Rangers' Loftus Road ground in 1981 – what was the sport?

30 In the early years of the FA Cup, the competition was won by Old Boys' sides from which two English public schools?

Athletics - Part 3

• QUESTIONS •

1 What is the full name of the eye-catching American sprinter nicknamed "Flo-Jo?"

2 Who said, on turning professional in 1974 . . . "Running for money doesn't make you run fast, it makes you run first."?

3 When was the Amateur Athletics Association formed?

4 What discipline is Jackie Joyner-Kersee best known for?

5 Which two clubs does Linford Christie run for?

6 Where is the finish of the London marathon?

7 What were the notorious GANEFO Games in Djakarta in 1963?

8 Where was the first marathon held in Britain and in what year?

9 How many laps of the track is the 10,000 metres event?

10 Who said: "I would give my right arm to be able to throw the javelin again."?

11 What Olympic event is Steve Ovett's brother known for?

12 In which events did Great Britain win their two track and field golds in the 1991 student games?

13 Who won a medal for Great Britain in the controversial women's 3,000 metres final at the Los Angeles Olympics in 1984?

14 In 1991, who finally broke Bob Beamon's 23 year old long jump world record of 8.90 metres?

15 Name Britain's trio in the men's 1,500 metres final in the 1984 Los Angeles games.

16 Name the two sprinters who forced Merlene Ottey into third place in the 1991 World Championships – her first defeat at 100 metres in 56 races?

17 Chinese shot putter Xinmei Sui, gold medalist in the 1991 World Student Games achieved what first?

18 What is the first event in the decathlon?

19 Which controversial athlete joined the Aldershot, Farnham and District Club in 1984?

20 Which country competes with the letters NIG on their race numbers?

21 Who was the men's 1,500 metres champion in the 1976 Montreal Olympics?

22 According to Brendan Foster, what was "the greatest run in the history of British distance running, men or women, anytime, anyplace, anywhere."?

23 At the Helsinki 1983 World Championships, who won the men's long jump?

24 Where did Sebastian Coe set the world 800 metres record in 1981?

25 When did Great Britain first win the Marathon World Cup team event?

26 How many gold medals did Great Britain win in the 1991 World Championships at Tokyo?

27 Banned in 1987, a drug called Probenecid is widely used for masking steroid traces. What is its proper medical use?

28 When was the first time that Great Britain won the European Cup?

29 At which track did Roger Bannister run the first sub four minute mile in 1954?

30 Why did Eva Klobukowska hit the headlines in 1961?

Cricket - Part 3

• QUESTIONS •

1 Who skippered South Africa to the 1992 World Cup semi-finals?

2 Who was the top Englishman in the 1991 first class batting averages?

3 Who made the 1,000th century to be scored in Test cricket, during a match between Australia and the West Indies in the 1968–69 season?

4 A new Test record was set in 1976 when India scored the highest ever fourth innings total to win a Test match – how many did they make and who were they playing?

5 When was the Marylebone Cricket Club founded?

6 Sri Lanka was one of two non-Test sides to compete in the first World Cup, in 1975 . . . which was the other?

7 Who was the man who bowled out the great Don Bradman for a duck in his final Test innings?

8 Who was the first cricketer to take 10 wickets and score 100 runs in the same Test match?

9 What unwanted record did Hampshire finally lay to rest when they appeared in the 1988 Benson and Hedges Cup final?

10 What is a bosie?

11 Which bowler took a wicket with his first ever ball in Test cricket in 1991?

12 Who were the first five English Test batsmen to score 7,000 runs in Tests?

13 Which international cricket competition was due to be staged in England in July 1992?

14 Former Australian cricket great, Bill O'Reilly, described watching his kitchen wall as "infinitely more interesting" than what?

15 Which two West Indian Test stars were sacked by Somerset in 1986?

16 What women's cricketing event was staged in 1973 – two years before the first similar competition for men?

17 Who hit the winning four for England in the 1991 Oval Test to tie the series with the West Indies?

18 What is a Nelson?

19 What was the International Cricket Conference known as before 1965?

20 Who was the first New Zealand batsman to score 4,000 runs in Tests?

21 How old was the legendary W.G. Grace when he made his final appearance for England in 1899 against Australia?

22 274 is the highest Test score made by a South African batsman. Who made it?

23 How many times has the World Cup cricket final been won by the side batting first?

24 Two West Indian greats both took their 100th wicket in Tests against England in the same match at Trinidad in 1974 – who were they?

25 Who was the only England bowler in the top 10 of the Coopers Deloitte ratings for Test players at the end of the 1991 season?

26 Which minor county knocked Derbyshire out of the 1991 Nat West Trophy in cricket's equivalent to a penalty shoot-out?

27 Which countries were visited by the women's English cricket team in 1934 on their first overseas tour?

28 Name the three teams which have beaten England in their first three World Cup final appearances?

29 Which New Zealand batsman batted for three consecutive days, but was still out for a duck?

30 What was Ian Botham talking about when he said: "At least they are getting better crowds for their pantomime than we are for ours."?

Origins of Sports

• QUESTIONS •

1 What popular pub game was originally devised as a training exercise for archers?

2 From which country does the Olympic sport of speed skating originate?

3 What invention of the 1880s was to put the sport of motor racing on the world map?

4 Which new water sport was invented in 1967?

5 Name the schoolboy who "picked up the ball and ran," giving birth to the game of rugby?

6 Golf is traditionally thought to have originated from Scotland. Many historians believe another country has a very strong claim – which one?

7 Which massively popular modern sport was thought up at the YMCA Training School in Springfield, Massachusetts, in 1891?

8 In 1895, at a meeting between 22 disgruntled clubs in Huddersfield, what sport was born?

9 Until approximately 1860, there were two Baseball "codes" – New York Baseball and Boston Baseball. What was the main difference?

10 What sport are Cambridge University students supposed to have created using a table, cigar boxes and corks in 1879?

11 The first recorded county cricket match was played at Dartford in 1709. Name the two sides involved?

12 What major rule change of 1906 revolutionised American Football and led to the game being played the way it is today?

13 In which city was Australian Rules football developed?

14 From which 12th to 13th century French game are most modern racquet sports descended?

15 In which country was the game of snooker developed by British Army officers?

16 The North American Indian game of baggataway developed into which modern sport, popular in Canada and among women worldwide?

17 What did American Fred Walter patent in 1900?

18 The sport of rackets is traditionally thought to have been invented in the early 19th century by debtors jailed at which prison?

19 In which country was water polo invented in 1870?

20 Which game of central Asian origin, dating back to 6BC, is now played regularly in Windsor Great Park?

21 Which modern Olympic sport had its origins in travelling circuses of the 18th and 19th centuries?

22 Which set of boxing rules laid down in 1838 stipulated that a bout had to take place within a roped-off ring, as nowadays?

23 From where does the sport badminton derive its name?

24 In which country did orienteering have its beginnings in 1918?

25 What sport did Captain James Cook observe natives of Tahiti and Oahu performing during his voyages to the South Seas in 1777 and 1778?

26 What game was invented at Harrow school by bored pupils hitting a rubber ball against a wall whilst waiting to get onto the rackets courts?

27 The forerunner of which fast modern game is thought to have been played in the early 1800s by the Micmac Indians in Nova Scotia?

28 Why was the popular forerunner of football banned by King Richard II in 1389?

29 All English thoroughbred racehorses should be traceable back to which three stallions imported to this country between 1689 and 1730?

30 Tennis in its modern form derived from a game introduced in 1873 by Major Walter Clopton Wingfield – under what name did he patent the game the following year?

Superstars – Part 2
• QUESTIONS •

1 Who, in American football, is known as "Sweetness"?

2 Which tycoon is well known for his obsession with breaking trans-Atlantic records involving balloons and boats?

3 Name the Hollywood star who ventured into the boxing ring as a professional fighter after becoming worried about his image as an actor.

4 West Indies cricket giant Viv Richards also gained international honours for his native Antigua at which other sport?

5 Name the three baseball players who have hit the all-time highest number of home runs.

6 In which year did East Germany's Katerina Witt win the Olympic gold medal for figure skating as well as the European and World Championships in the same discipline?

7 In the 1984 Los Angeles Olympics Carl Lewis matched Jesse Owens' four gold medals from 52 years before, at the 1936 Munich games. What were the events?

8 Between which years did the great Joe Louis, the longest reigning world heavyweight boxing champion, hold his title?

9 Which British sporting champion went missing in February 1983 and was never seen again?

10 Which rugby union player said in 1991: "I am still an amateur of course, but I became rugby's first millionaire five years ago."?

11 Up to the beginning of 1992, Jack Nicklaus had won a total of 18 majors . . . which one had he won most often?

12 Which member of the rampaging Real Madrid side of the 1950s and 1960s scored a staggering 49 goals in European Cup competitions.

13 Who is the only cricketer to have scored 300 runs or more in a single day of a Test match?

14 Which Formula One motor racing driver is also an accomplished golfer, who once played in the Australian Open.

15 In which year did Muhammad Ali become the first boxer to win the world heavyweight title three times?

16 Which team did Canadian ice hockey ace Mario Lemieux lead to the Stanley Cup in 1991?

17 In what sport was Bernard Hinault a French national hero?

18 Who was the 44-year-old Texas Rangers pitcher who threw the seventh no hitter of his career in 1991, three more than the next best record?

19 Which great Italian sprinter's 1979 200 metres world record time of 19.72 seconds was still intact at the beginning of the 1992 season?

20 Which skier has won the highest number of World Cup races?

21 Who was the only footballer to get into the top 10 earners in British sport for 1990?

22 Name the British pop star who owned the yacht, Drum, which sank in the 1985 Fastnet race?

23 Which USA basketball player shocked the world in 1991 with the revelation that he was HIV positive?

24 Which footballer scored 37 hat-tricks in his football league career?

25 To the nearest 10, how many National Football League gridiron players averaged salaries of more than $1 million in 1991?

26 What do the following Olympic medallists have in common . . . Johnny Weismuller, Herman Brix and Buster Crabbe?

27 Undefeated world heavyweight champion Rocky Marciano retired without ever losing a fight . . . how many did he win in his boxing career?

28 Which jockey holds the world record for the number of winners ridden in a career, with a total of 8,833?

29 Who was baseball player Randy Moffitt's famous tennis-playing sister?

30 Which footballing great's England career ended when he was substituted in the 1970 World Cup quarter final?

World Champions (UK)
• QUESTIONS •

1 In which year did Jayne Torvill and Christopher Dean win their last ice dancing world title?

2 Who were Britain's World Professional Snooker champions in 1989, 1990 and 1991?

3 At which cycling discipline were Britain's Tony Doyle and Colin Sturgess world champions in 1986 and 1989 respectively?

4 Who rode Henderson Milton to consecutive successes in showjumping's Volvo World Cup in 1990 and 1991?

5 Who was the first British golfer to win the World Matchplay Championship?

6 At what weight did British judo star Karen Briggs win the World Judo Championships in 1984, 1986 and 1989?

7 In which year did Martin Brundle drive a Jaguar to his first World Sportscar Championship?

8 Up until and including 1991, how many times had a non-British player won the World Professional Darts Championship?

9 Who were Britain's only ever world bobsleigh champions?

10 What did Martine Le Moignan become the first ever Briton to win in 1989?

11 Which British rugby league side won the World Sevens Championship in Sydney early in 1992?

12 Who won Britain's only gold at the 1987 World Athletics Championships in Rome?

13 Which British driver has won the Formula One Drivers' championship most times?

14 Between its inception in 1870 and 1991, how many times did a non-Briton win the World Professional Billiards Championships?

15 When did David Bryant win his first outdoor World Bowls Championship?

16 At what weight did Maurice Hope become Britain's first-ever world champion in 1979?

17 Who was Britain's first Formula One drivers champion?

18 How many times has Great Britain won the Rugby League World Cup?

19 Which rower partnered Andrew Holmes to the coxless pairs world championships in 1987 and Matthew Pinsent to the same title in 1991?

20 Between 1932 and 1950, six British boxers won world titles and maintained uninterrupted domination at which weight?

21 What bike did Great Britain's Carl Fogarty ride to the Formula One motorcycle world championship in 1988?

22 At which two events did British swimmer David Wilkie win the world title in 1975?

23 At what sport did Britain's John Walters win the world championship in 1991, the year after his compatriot Robert Fulford won the same title?

24 England won the Swaythling Cup in 1953 to win the world men's championships for the first and only time at which sport?

25 Who became the women's World Rally Driving champion for Great Britain in 1991?

26 Which English angler won the World Freshwater Championships in 1990 and 1991?

27 What world title did Wendy Norman win for Britain in 1982?

28 Which is the only British country to win a world title at curling?

29 In what year did Bob Fitzsimmons win the world heavyweight title and when did he lose it . . . to become the last Briton to be world champion at the division?

30 Which world title did the Black Dog Boozers, from Crawley, Sussex, hold uninterrupted from 1985 to 1991, before losing it to the Moonshiners?

Rivals

• QUESTIONS •

1 Between which counties are cricket's Roses matches played?

2 Which two football teams contest the Edinburgh derby?

3 A hybrid game of rugby and football was played between two colleges in the USA in 1875 ... what did the encounter develop into?

4 Golf's 1991 Ryder Cup prompted who to say, "Next week, we'll still have the best players in the world."?

5 In which year was the Ashes rivalry between England and Australia born?

6 In 1991, which two Formula One drivers had 90 minutes of "peace talks" in a bid to heal their long-running feud?

7 What unprecedented step was taken to accommodate the north London derby FA Cup semi-final between Arsenal and Tottenham in 1991?

8 Which two heavyweight boxers contested the 1975 "Thrilla in Manila" world title fight, which marked the culmination of a long rivalry?

9 What tragic events scarred the Old Firm football clash between Rangers and Celtic at Ibrox in January 1971?

10 Name the Liverpool goalkeeper of the 1920's who had a great rivalry with Everton's record-breaking goalscorer Dixie Dean.

11 Which two great international Rugby Union rivals vie for the Bedisloe Cup?

12 A long-standing rivalry between two great British athletes began in their much awaited first race against each other in the 1978 European Championships 800 metres – who were they?

13 Which two American football teams jostle for the headlines in Los Angeles?

14 Why was the 1991 Scottish Cup final between Motherwell and Dundee United a family affair?

15 Which yacht broke the USA's 113 year stranglehold on the America's Cup and gave birth to an age of legal wrangling and feuding?

16 Which South American football nation was disqualified from the 1986 World Cup finals after an incident in which their goalkeeper faked serious injury in a bid to have a qualifying match abandoned?

17 How were Liverpool's Gary Gillespie and Everton's Stuart McCall able to continue their footballing rivalries after both were transferred in the same month in 1991?

18 What do the Greyhounds and the LX Club contest fiercely each year?

19 How many times have Chris Evert and Martina Navratilova battled out a Wimbledon singles finals?

20 Which two New York baseball teams contested the World Series in no less than six seasons?

21 What is the trophy that the England and Scotland rugby union play for each year in the Five Nations tournament?

22 Which two public schools play an annual cricket match at Lords?

23 Intense rivalries between which two countries led to an Olympic water polo contest becoming "a boxing match underwater" at the 1956 Melbourne games?

24 What are the names of the two great Madrid football clubs?

25 When did Liverpool and Everton first cross swords in an all Merseyside Wembley cup final?

26 To the nearest thousand, how many of Australian batting legend Don Bradman's 6,996 Test runs were scored against England?

27 In which year was the only dead heat between Oxford and Cambridge in the Boat Race?

28 At the end of their legendary 1981 world title boxing bout, with what words did Roberto Duran surrender to Sugar Ray Leonard?

29 What incident involving brothers Greg and Trevor Chappell during a Benson and Hedges World Series Cup cricket match intensified the strong rivalry that already existed between New Zealand and Australia?

30 In 1984, Pat Butcher of the Times newspaper described it as: "The most famous collision since the Titanic and the iceberg" – what was he referring to?

Trophies

• QUESTIONS •

1 In what way is the FA Cup trophy not unique?

2 With what world famous slippery slope would you associate the Brabazon Trophy?

3 The winners of what are presented with the Vince Lombardi Trophy?

4 Who plays for the Curtis Cup?

5 What is the oldest sporting trophy in the world still regularly contested?

6 What form of transport is raced to contest the Southern Cross Cup?

7 Who sponsored the 1992 cricket World Cup?

8 With what sport do you associate the Breeders Cup?

9 Who are the perpetual holders of the Jules Rimet Trophy?

10 What do boxers usually get as trophies?

11 What animals race for the BBC Television Trophy?

12 In which sport is the North Sea Cup contested?

13 By what extremely long-winded name was Football's UEFA Cup originally known?

14 The winners of the women's Indoor Bowling Association inter-club championship lift which trophy?

15 What is the ultimate prize in North America's National Hockey League?

16 In 1971, the USA beat England to win the first Coronation Cup in which sport?

17 The King George V Gold Cup and the Queen Elizabeth II Cup are won at which equestrian event?

18 With what sport do you associate India's Ranji Trophy and Pakistan's Quaid-e-Azam Trophy?

19 In which event do Oxford and Cambridge Universities compete for the Bowring Bowl?

20 In Table Tennis, what cup do the winners of the men's World Team Championships receive?

21 The Brownlow Medal is the highest individual award in which antipodean sport?

22 To which individual is American Football's highly coveted Heisman Trophy awarded?

23 What trophy is the winning Formula One motor racing team awarded at the end of the season?

24 At which event in the English social calendar do some of the competitors vie for the Silver Goblets and Nickalls?

25 Kingussie won the 1991 Camanachd Cup . . . but in which sport?

26 What trophy did the challengers in yachting's 1992 America's Cup have to win to get the chance to race for the big prize?

27 Women contest the Uber Cup in which sport?

28 Which player wins Rugby League's Lance Todd Trophy?

29 Apart from a huge silver trophy and a massive cheque, what else is awarded to the US Masters champion?

30 Which football cup competition would you be watching if Carthusians and Malvernians were contesting the final?

Weird and Wonderful

• QUESTIONS •

1 Which communist leader shunned an offer to play major league baseball in order to pursue his political ideology?

2 What unusual incident happened to Spanish golfer Jose Maria Olazabal on the first fairway at Birkdale in the 1991 British Open?

3 Who skippered Great Britain's 1971 Admiral's Cup yachting campaign?

4 Which great composer was also a world champion at show jumping?

5 What did Australian cricketer Merv Hughes insure for £200,000 after signing up to do beer commercials?

6 During the 1991 World Student Games at Sheffield, three Mozambican athletes out on a training run were hauled in by police – why?

7 Why was Ingemar Johansson disqualified in the 1952 Helsinki Olympics heavyweight boxing final?

8 How did the authorities envisage putting the Oval cricket ground to good use during World War II?

9 Why was the start of the 1991 Trans Australian race for solar powered cars delayed?

10 Why do some motorcycle racers perform bizarre rituals when they wear new leathers for the first time?

11 For what bizarre reason was footballer Ruben Olivera sent off in a Uruguayan First Division clash in 1991?

12 A legendary lawman refereed Britain's future world heavyweight champion boxer, Bob Fitzsimmons, in a bout in 1896 – who was he?

13 Which famous author invented the red golf ball for use in snowy conditions?

14 Which sport, originally called "mintonette", was invented for businessmen who found basketball too vigorous?

15 Which international disaster of 1912 was presaged by BOTH the Oxford and Cambridge crews sinking in the Boat Race just two weeks before it happened?

16 How long does the Olympic three day equestrian event last?

17 In the 1904 St Louis Olympics, the USA had a clean sweep of medals in a croquet-like game called roque on the only occasion it appeared in the games . . . what took the shine off their achievement?

18 In 1991, what event did Sian Evans win at Llanwrtyd Wells, in Wales, in a time of two minutes and 14 seconds?

19 Spectator Mike Pierce kicked three field goals during an interval at an Indianapolis Colts American football game to win what for almost 60,000 spectactors?

20 Why was Fred Lorz disqualified after "winning" the 1904 Olympic Marathon?

21 American jockey Sylvester Carmouche was sent to jail after cheating during a race in Louisiana – what had he done?

22 Pope John Paul II was once an accomplished footballer – what position did he play?

23 The tiny French village of Moncrabeau stages the world championship in which "sport" every three years?

24 How did British 10,000 metre runner Carl Thackery injure himself while training in Mexico in 1991?

25 The Olympic doubles tennis champion of the 1924 Paris games, USA's Norris Williams, was a survivor from which disaster 12 years before?

26 Muggsy Bogues made his basketball debut for the Charlotte Hornets in the USA's NBA Eastern Conference in 1991 – what made him stand out?

27 Which Grand National is run over a distance of just 474 metres?

28 Which Gothic horror novelist was also an accomplished competitor in Victorian walking races?

29 What was extraordinary about the mile race that Johan Landsman won in just over four minutes at Secunda in South Africa in 1991?

30 What was the connection between all of the medallists – gold, silver and bronze – in the tug of war at the 1908 London Olympics?

The Answers

General Part 1: Answers

1 Sue Brown, the 1981 Oxford Cox. **2** Five. **3** Vulcanised rubber. **4** They have to be fillies and three years old. **5** Tourist Trophy. **6** Belgian. **7** New York Yankees. **8** Leighton Rees. **9** James Callaghan. **10** A canoeing event. **11** Women's football. **12** It is the same as bowls, but the green has a hump in the middle. **13** The Grand National. **14** Riding, fencing, shooting, swimming and running. **15** Real tennis. **16** Baseball. **17** Fencing. **18** A horse which has never won a race. **19** The Maracana Stadium in Rio de Janeiro. **20** Every two years. **21** Duathlon. **22** Their hands. **23** New Zealand. **24** Clay pigeon shooting. **25** L'Escargot. **26** They were, or are, women Formula One racing drivers. **27** Rugby union, rugby league and football. **28** They were all standing in the country's elections and the law required equal coverage for all candidates, sports heroes or otherwise. **29** 1987. **30** Australian Rules football.

Football Part 1: Answers

1 Scunthorpe United, Liverpool, Southampton, Newcastle United. **2** Cardiff City. They beat Arsenal 1–0 in 1927. **3** Barcelona. **4** Exeter City and Newcastle United. **5** Ronnie Moran (caretaker), Kenny Dalglish, Joe Fagan, Bob Paisley, Bill Shankly. **6** Ian Porterfield, for Sunderland v Leeds United. **7** Bon Accord. **8** Diego Maradona. **9** Aston Villa (1981) and Arsenal (1989). **10** Hibernian. **11** Joe Mercer. **12** Rangers, Celtic, Aberdeen, Dundee United. **13** Feyenoord. **14** Allan Clarke (1980–82), Eddie Gray (1982–85), Billy Bremner (1985–88). **15** George Best. **16** Brian Clough. **17** Clive Allen, in 1980. **18** Denis Law, playing for City against his former club. **19** Mark Crossley, for Nottingham Forest v Spurs, 1991. **20** West Bromwich Albion. **21** Glasgow Rangers. **22** They became Manchester United, in 1902.

23 At Everton's Goodison Park in 1973. They beat Northern Ireland 2-1. **24** Alex Ferguson, with Aberdeen (1983) and Manchester United (1991). **25** Queen's Park Rangers in 1967. They beat West Bromwich Albion 3-2. **26** BBC commentator John Motson on Wimbledon's FA Cup final victory over Liverpool in 1988. **27** Bury. **28** Serie A. **29** Arsenal and West Ham United. **30** They became the first league club of the year to sack their manager, Terry Butcher.

Rugby Union: Answers

1 Twickenham (England), Parc des Princes (France), Lansdowne Road (Ireland), Murrayfield (Scotland) and Cardiff Arms Park (Wales). **2** The Eagles. **3** Newport. **4** Ireland's Ralph Keyes. **5** Five, by the 1991 England Grand Slam side. **6** Mike Teague. **7** 1871. **8** Rory Underwood and Dewi Morris. **9** Graham Bachop was New Zealand's scrum-half. His brother Steve played fly-half for Western Samoa. **10** Australia's Michael Lynagh. **11** Roger Uttley and Andy Ripley. **12** Namibia. **13** David Kirk, who led New Zealand to World Cup glory in 1987. **14** A cockerel. **15** Newport. **16** Northampton (all three are nicknamed "the Saints"). **17** Micky Skinner. **18** Jeremy Guscott. **19** Romania – the match was in Bucharest. **20** There were accusations of professionalism in French rugby. **21** Carston Catcheside, in 1924. **22** Prince Alexander Obolensky. **23** The reigning Olympic champions are the USA, who won gold in the 1924 Paris games, the last time rugby was on the Olympic agenda. **24** Due to superstition, Bath do not play with a number 13, so the centre wears the wing's number 14 shirt . . . and so on. **25** The Varsity match. **26** Fishing. **27** Mike Harrison. **28** Tim Rodber. **29** The USA. They beat the England women by 19-6. **30** French prop Gregoire Lascube (detective inspector) was dismissed for stamping on England lock Martin Bayfield (police constable) in the ugly

1992 Grand Slam encounter at Parc des Princes.

Motor Sport: Answers

1 None. **2** Le Mans. **3** 1985. **4** Jack Brabham himself. **5** Joey Dunlop, in 1987. **6** Ronnie Peterson. **7** Carlos Sainz. **8** Argentinian. **9** Jody Scheckter, in 1979, driving for Ferrari. **10** 1906, at Le Mans. **11** Phil. **12** Ford, with more than 150. **13** 350cc and 500cc. **14** Nürburgring. Arturio Merzario. **15** He had been told that, at 6ft, he was too tall to drive Formula One cars. **16** Japan. **17** Bertrand Gachot. **18** Mike Hawthorn. **19** Estoril. **20** Jackie Stewart. **21** Carlos Pace. **22** It began, and ended, in Rome. **23** Aston Martin, in 1959. **24** Jochen Rindt, in 1970. **25** They all died during the TT races on the Isle of Man. **26** Ferrari, eight times. **27** Jim Clark, Graham Hill and Jackie Stewart. **28** There was an alarmingly high number of crashes involving competitors. **29** John Kocinski. **30** The Spanish Grand Prix.

Athletics Part 1: Answers

1 On your marks. **2** Lynch. **3** International Amateur Athletics Federation. **4** 800 metres. **5** 5,000 metres. **6** It had joint winners ... Dick Beardsley and Inge Simonsen. **7** Eric Liddell. **8** Zola Budd (1,500 metres) and Mary Decker (mile). **9** 26 miles 385 yards. **10** Shot, discus and javelin. **11** 15 mph. **12** Four. **13** Chris Brasher. **14** Steve Cram. **15** Kriss Akabusi. **16** 20 metres. **17** Ethiopian distance runner Miruts Yifter. **18** Dick Fosbury – the Fosbury flop. **19** Newbold. **20** The Athletics Congress. **21** Boston. **22** Algeria. **23** Finland's Tiina Lillak. **24** Greg Foster, of the USA. **25** Ben Johnson's coach, Charlie Francis. **26** The 4 × 400 metres relay. **27** Pole vault. **28** Harold Abra-

hams, in the 1924 Paris games. **29** Matthew Yates.
30 The World Student Games.

Boxing: Answers

1 Steve Cruz. **2** An uppercut punch. **3** IBF, WBA, WBC, WBO. **4** Canada. **5** Tommy Farr. **6** British lightweight champion, Carl Crook. **7** The Marquess of Queensbury. **8** Light heavyweight. **9** Percy Commet of Ghana. **10** 175 pounds. **11** Light heavyweight. **12** Tony Tucker. **13** Round seven. **14** Don King. **15** He had lifted a long-standing ban on professional fights in the Soviet Union. **16** Mike Tyson, Tim Witherspoon and James "Bonecrusher" Smith (Smith became champion after defeating Bruno). **17** He was blind in one eye. **18** Straw-weight. **19** Primo Carnera of Italy. **20** Honeyghan despatched Gene Hatcher in just 45 seconds of their welterweight fight in 1987. **21** Himself. **22** USA's Ted Lowry. **23** Pigeons. **24** Welterweight. **25** Frank Warren. **26** Tokyo. **27** Tim "Doc" Anderson. **28** Ken Norton – he was declared champion by the WBC after Leon Spinks refused to fight him. He failed to defend his "title." **29** They are the only world champions to die while defending their titles. **30** James Callaghan.

Cricket Part 1: Answers

1 William Gilbert. **2** Nottinghamshire. **3** The Wooloongabba. **4** 1932–33. **5** Tom Moody. **6** Lahore, Pakistan. **7** Middlesex, in 1980. **8** Pakistan. **9** It was shared by Middlesex and Kent. **10** Bowled, LBW, caught, stumped, run out, hit the ball twice, obstructing the field, hit wicket, timed out, handling the ball. **11** South Africa. **12** All his victims were out LBW. **13** 903 for seven, against Australia, 1938. **14** He was just 15 years old. **15** They lost to the combined Oxford and Cambridge universities' side, by seven wickets. **16** Eight times, including a shared title with Lancashire. **17** Neither, it was the first time ever that a Test match was tied. **18** 90 runs. **19** India, in 1985. **20** 28 inches. **21** "Fiery" Fred Trueman. **22** He played in an F.A. Cup final and he held the World Long Jump Record for 21 years. **23** Len Hutton of Yorkshire, when he captained England against Australia in 1953. **24** Sir Frank Worrell. **25** Chris Tavare. **26** 21 July, 1884. England played Australia. **27** 197. **28** Waqar Younis. **29** White Heather. **30** 1963, when the distinction between amateur and professional status was abolished.

Olympics - Part 1: Answers

1 Baron Pierre de Coubertin. **2** Rome. **3** They invaded Afghanistan. **4** Never. **5** Hockey, rowing, swimming, yachting and shooting. **6** Ben Johnson. **7** Romania's Nadia Comaneci. **8** 1960. **9** Foil. **10** It was held outdoors. **11** The wedding was at the height of the Cold War, but Hal Connolly was American and his bride, Olga Fitova, was Czechoslovakian. **12** Long jump and 100 metres. **13** None. **14** Munich 1972. **15** Joe Frazier (1964) and George Foreman (1968). **16** Lord Burghley. He won the 400 metres hurdles in the 1928 games at Amsterdam. **17** Paris 1900. **18** Dave Warren. **19** She was the first woman to light the Olympic flame. **20** Helsinki 1952. **21** St Louis and Los Angeles (twice). **22** Goodwill. **23** Epee, foil and sabre. **24** Five. **25** Tiina Lillak. **26** 9.79 seconds. **27** Baseball and badminton. **28** Triple jump. **29** The summer games were held in Melbourne, but, because of Australia's strict quarantine laws, horses could not be taken into the country. As a result, the equestrian events took place in Stockholm. **30** He ran the entire race carrying a bible.

Football World Cup - Part 1:
Answers

1 1970. **2** Gary Lineker, Peter Beardsley, David Platt, Stuart Pearce, Chris Waddle. **3** Australia. **4** West Germany's Franz Beckenbauer. **5** It is the only time that England, Scotland, Wales and Northern Ireland have all qualified together. **6** Czechoslovakia. **7** The teams turned up in identical strips. The match was delayed so that Hungary could buy a new kit. **8** Brazil. **9** North Korea. **10** Mario Kempes of Argentina. **11** Pickles. **12** El Salvador. **13** England. **14** Six. **15** Andreas Brehme, for West Germany against Argentina. **16** Cameroon. **17** Iraq. **18** Poland. **19** Argentina. **20** They had fielded ineligible players during a World Cup Youth tournament. **21** Zaire, in 1974. **22** Algeria. **23** Just Fontaine, with 13 for France. **24** West Germany. They now play as Germany since the unification of East and West. **25** Italy's Dino Zoff, in 1982. **26** 17 years and 42 days. **27** Chile "played" the match in Santiago without the Soviets, who refused to participate in protest against a revolution. **28** Algeria. **29** There was a final pool involving the last four teams. Uruguay beat Brazil in the decider. **30** He was the referee who allowed Diego Maradona's "Hand-of-God" goal.

Superstars - Part 1: Answers

1 Red Rum. **2** £440,000 for Martin Offiah. **3** Wayne Gretzky. **4** He was a matador. **5** Kent Desormeaux. **6** Montreal 1976. **7** Serge Blanco. **8** Joe Davis. **9** Imola, Italy. **10** Juan Manuel Fangio. **11** Seven (four individual and three relay). **12** Gary Sobers. **13** Light heavyweight, super middleweight, middleweight, junior middleweight and welterweight. **14** Russia's Igor Shalimov. **15** Real Madrid. **16** Ian Woosnam. **17** John

McEnroe. **18** Dennis Connor. **19** Monica Seles. **20** Aston Villa's David Platt, sold to Bari for £5.5 million in 1991. **21** 1980 and 1981. **22** Elton John. **23** Charistmatic USA golfer Lee Trevino. **24** Mark Gastineau. **25** Roberto Baggio. **26** Jahangir Khan. **27** They did not have to sweat through the whole tournament. The holder only had to ward off a challenge from the winner of the open contest. **28** Burt Reynolds. **29** Kim Hughes, in 1981. **30** Sean Connery, the former James Bond.

General - Part 2: Answers

1 June. **2** The Hurlingham Club. **3** Henry Cooper and Muhammad Ali. **4** Basketball. **5** Four. **6** It is where you throw your darts from. **7** Winter rowing competitions. **8** A ball game played in the Basque country. **9** The King George V Handicap. **10** Horse racing courses. **11** Dorset. **12** He was the first male umpire to officiate a netball international. **13** Vault, beam, floor and asymmetric bars. **14** Cycling. **15** Royal Lytham and St Annes. **16** Jahangir and Jansher. **17** Yokozuna. **18** Canada. **19** He was the first overseas player to play for Yorkshire. **20** The winner of the race, held just five days before a General Election, was called Party Politics. **21** Junior league American football, where the emphasis is on safety. **22** Steinlager. **23** Australian rules football. **24** The British Formula One Grand Prix. **25** Golf clubs. **26** It will host the first ever World Cup indoor football match. **27** Tour de France, Tour of Italy and Tour of Spain. **28** The women's British Open squash championships. **29** She was the first woman to wear a bikini in official competition. **30** He was the first Yugoslav to win a Blue.

Football - Part 2: Answers

1 She was the first woman official at a football league match. **2** Kevin Keegan. **3** Eight feet. **4** White City. **5** Everton and Tranmere Rovers. **6** Hungary, in 1953. **7** Senegal. **8** Tottenham, in 1961 and 1962. **9** St Johnstone. **10** Nottingham Forest manager Brian Clough. **11** Aston Villa (Dr Josef Vengloss). **12** They both had long spells at Southampton. **13** Liverpool, Sunderland, Portsmouth and Norwich. **14** Birmingham City. **15** Bury (1900 and 1903). **16** Belgium. **17** Fourth Division Wrexham's Steve Watkin. **18** Chris Nichol, in 1991. **19** Hunslet. **20** The Toyota Cup. **21** Gordon Strachan. **22** Manchester City. **23** Peter Shilton, Bobby Moore, Bobby Charlton and Billy Wright. **24** Colombia. **25** Robert Maxwell. **26** Crystal Palace, Arsenal, West Ham, Queens Park Rangers, Tottenham and Chelsea. **27** Tom Finney, of Preston and England. **28** Federation Internationale de Football Association. **29** Luton Town. **30** Roger Hunt made way for Jimmy Greaves.

Rugby League: Answers

1 Jonathan Davies. **2** John Player Special Trophy. **3** Papua New Guinea's test side. **4** Leeds. **5** 1959. **6** Once. **7** The highest semi-final points score, with 71. **8** 19–12. **9** 1906. **10** All Golds. **11** 61. **12** 1978. **13** Bradford Northern. **14** Seven. **15** Queensland and New South Wales. **16** Rugby a treize. **17** Rosslyn Park and Ipswich. **18** 1954 and 1972. **19** Vince Karalius. **20** Southend Invicta. **21** 1946. **22** Alan Prescott. **23** Papua New Guinea. **24** Bradford Northern's Simon Tuffs. **25** Gus Risman, with Workington Town. **26** The Harry Sunderland Trophy. **27** Cawoods. **28** Trans-Tasman Cup. **29** Keith Elwell. **30** Dewsbury.

Horse Racing: Answers

1 Five. 2 Queen Anne. 3 One mile and a half. 4 Gulfland. 5 It was run on a Friday. 6 Sir Gordon Richards, Doug Smith, Lester Piggott, Willie Carson and Pat Eddery. 7 The St Leger, in 1776. 8 1982. 9 The Melbourne Cup. 10 Anne, Duchess of Westminster. 11 Newmarket. 12 He became the first jockey to ride winners at three different courses on the same day. 13 Epsom, Newmarket and Doncaster. 14 Diomed, in 1780. 15 1947. 16 Jersey. 17 Great Nephew. 18 Reynoldstown, in 1935 and 1936. 19 Roberto. 20 Wincanton. 21 Henry Cecil and Sheik Mohammed. 22 The Kentucky Derby, the Belmontt Stakes and the Preakness Stakes. 23 Toulon. 24 Prix du Jockey Club. 25 Although the winner shared the same name as the race's sponsors, Seagram, the chairman of the company had twice refused to buy it. 26 The Swedish Derby. 27 Jonjo O'Neill, in 1980. 28 Snow Bride. 29 Jack Berry. 30 500–1.

Athletics Part 2: Answers

1 Kirsty Wade. 2 The firing of a gun. 3 Leroy Burrell and Dennis Mitchell. 4 Helsinki. 5 Jarmila Kratoch-vilova, of Czechoslovakia. 6 Kenya. 7 1991. 8 1991. 9 Australia's Betty Cuthbert. 10 Eamonn Coghlan. 11 Mary Decker. 12 100 metres hurdles, shot, high jump, javelin, long jump, 200 metres and 800 metres. 13 1986 and 1982. 14 Greta Weitz and Joan Benoit. 15 New Zealand. 16 Said Aouita. 17 One – Women's Triple Jump. 18 Willie Banks. 19 The Queen. 20 Pole vault. 21 1988 (Jackie Joyner-Kersee). 22 Shot put. 23 98-year-old Dimitris Iordanidis. 24 1988. 25 Judy Oakes. 26 Alan Wells. 27 Eight. 28 Tessa Sanderson. 29 Liz McColgan, in the 1991 New York marathon. 30 Starting blocks.

Snooker: Answers

1 James Wattana and John Parrott. **2** Fred and Joe were brothers, Steve is no relation. **3** 36. **4** Walter Donaldson, in 1947. **5** Ivory. **6** Surfing. **7** His 16–18 defeat by Steve Davis in 1984. **8** Scotland's Stephen Hendry, who was first, Northern Ireland's Dennis Taylor (ninth) and Doug Mountjoy of Wales (tenth). **9** Melbourne, Australia. **10** Karen Corr and Stacey Hillyard. **11** The black ball. **12** Alex Higgins. **13** 1986. **14** Cliff Thorburn. **15** Six pounds and ten shillings. **16** 27. **17** Patsy Fagan. **18** Three feet. **19** Alex Higgins, Fred Davis and John Pullman. **20** John Spencer, in 1977. **21** Joe Davis. **22** Alex Higgins. **23** Ray Reardon. **24** Coral and Tennents. **25** Two and one-sixteenth inches. **26** They are or were all left-handed. **27** Jimmy White. **28** John Spencer. **29** Thailand's James Wattana. **30** Steve James.

Hockey: Answers

1 1971. **2** Nine inches. **3** Scotland. **4** Milton Keynes. **5** 13. **6** Blackheath. **7** Hounslow, East Grinstead, Teddington and Southgate. **8** 1886. **9** Their group match against West Germany, who they beat in the final. **10** Four yards. **11** David Archer. **12** Great Britain were let in as first reserves after a boycott led to the Soviet team dropping out. **13** Holland. **14** England's World Cup final clash with Australia. **15** 1973. **16** Slough's Paul Barber. **17** Pakistan. **18** Glasgow Western. **19** South Korea. **20** India. **21** 1979. **22** It was the first time that a league match had been allowed to take place under floodlights. **23** Best Goalkeeper of the Tournament. **24** Bombay. **25** The USA. **26** Atletico Terrassa. **27** Ric Charlesworth. **28** Veryan Pappin and Sam Martin. **29** Manchester United. **30** The first president of the Hockey Association was the

Duke of Clarence, whom many believe to have been Jack the Ripper.

Tennis: Answers

1 Patrick. 2 There was play on the middle Sunday.
3 Kevin Curran, in 1985. 4 None. He lost three sets to tie-breaks. 5 He won four games while going down in straight sets. 6 Moffitt. 7 1984. Jimmy Connors against John McEnroe. 8 Kooyong. 9 The 1968 US Open and the 1977 Wimbledon titles. 10 She played Cinderella in a pantomime at Stockport. 11 There are no size or weight restrictions. 12 US doubles champion Dwight Davis.
13 Australia's Wendy Turnbull. 14 The 1976 French Open.
15 Yannick Noah. 16 Six times. 17 Jana Novotna.
18 Peter Doohan. 19 Maureen Connolly, Margaret Court and Steffi Graf. 20 It was the first five set women's match in a major tournament for 90 years. 21 The French Open. 22 The 1961 women's final, between Angela Mortimer and Christine Truman. 23 Chris Evert's.
24 The double-strung "spaghetti" racquet. 25 Switzerland. 26 Vitas Gerulitis. 27 Ilie Nastase, Jimmy Connors (twice), Roscoe Tanner and John McEnroe.
28 1981 (Australian Open). 29 Mats Wilander (French), Boris Becker (Wimbledon) and Michael Chang (French).
30 99.

Cricket - Part 2: Answers

1 Melbourne. 2 Andy Sandham (325 for England v West Indies – Kingston in the 1929/30 Series). 3 David Shepherd. 4 Narendra Hirwani. 5 Somerset. 6 Middlesex. 7 Andy Goram. 8 Sir Richard Hadlee. 9 Peter May. 10 The Neville Ground, Bristol. 11 Chris Pringle. 12 Wilfred Rhodes. 13 Derek Underwood. 14 Malcolm Nash. 15 Brian Close. 16 The

Parks (Oxford) and Fenners. **17** Run out, going for his 500. **18** Geoff Boycott. **19** Lancashire, in 1990. **20** Brendan Kuruppu. **21** New Zealand. **22** He needed four, but scored nought. **23** Richard/Dale Hadlee, Geoff/Peter Howarth, John/Brendan Bracewell, Martin/Jeff Crowe. **24** 1864. **25** Robert Vance. **26** Goatacre. **27** Dennis Lillee. **28** Jack Russell. **29** Chris Cowdrey, John Emburey, Ian Botham. **30** Chris Broad.

Olympics - Part 2: Answers

1 USA swimmers Nancy Hogshead and Carrie Steinseifer. **2** Czechoslovakia. **3** Renald Knysh. **4** 800 metres. **5** Greco-Roman and Freestyle. **6** Great Britain. **7** 1894. **8** 72 years old (and 280 days). **9** They were special interim games to celebrate 10 years of modern Olympic competition. **10** London 1908. **11** Rome 1960. **12** Modern Pentathlon – he tried to cheat in the fencing discipline. **13** Athens. **14** French. **15** Australia's Glynis Nunn, at Los Angeles in 1984. **16** Amsterdam 1928. **17** Four-man bobsleigh and boxing (light heavyweight). **18** Once – Melbourne 1956. **19** Los Angeles 1984. **20** 11. **21** Emil Zatopek, of Czechoslovakia, in Helsinki 1952. **22** Finnish. **23** Showjumping. **24** She won both the 200 metres and 400 metres. **25** Jurgen Straub. **26** An extra 400 metres lap was run because of an error by an official. **27** The 4 × 100 metres relay, by the USA. **28** The 100 metres was run in less 10 seconds and the 200 metres in less than 20 seconds, both for the first time at an Olympics. **29** He was so slow in his 10,000 metres heat that he finished six laps behind the next slowest runner. **30** Painting, music, sculpture, literature and architecture.

Football World Cup - Part 2:
Answers

1 BBC Television commentator Kenneth Wolstenholme.
2 Sweden. **3** New Order . . . with some help from the England squad. **4** Italy. 1-0. **5** Holland (1974 and 1978), West Germany (1982 and 1986). **6** Uruguay.
7 Peter Shilton. **8** He was the first to miss a penalty.
9 Colombia. Civil unrest forced the tournament to be moved to Mexico. **10** One, England. **11** They did not win a single match in open play. They drew three group matches and beat Romania on penalties in the second round. They eventually lost to Italy. **12** 1958. **13** Montevideo. **14** Morocco. **15** Jairzinho of Brazil. **16** Jack Taylor. **17** Gerry Armstrong. **18** The USA, with a 1-0 victory. **19** Zaire, Holland, New Zealand and Sweden. **20** 1958 and 1970. **21** Italy's Paolo Rossi. **22** Sweden (1958) and Brazil (1950). **23** Willie Ormond, Ally MacLeod, Jock Stein, Alex Ferguson, Andy Roxburgh. **24** The 199,854 who watched Uruguay play Brazil in 1950. **25** 1934, 1966, 1978. **26** Neither. The World Cup has gone seven times each to Europe and South America. **27** Peter Beardsley, in the 3-0 defeat of Paraguay. **28** The matches in question were due to be played on Sundays. The team played the games anyway. **29** Because they were refused permission to play in bare feet. **30** Gordon Banks, Ray Wilson, George Cohen, Jack Charlton, Bobby Moore, Nobby Stiles, Martin Peters, Alan Ball, Bobby Charlton, Geoff Hurst, Roger Hunt.

Winter Sports: Answers

1 The USSR. **2** Eddie "the Eagle" Edwards. **3** Stefan Eberharter. **4** Nordic and Alpine. **5** St Moritz.
6 Downhill, slalom, giant slalom and super giant slalom.
7 Katarina Witt. **8** Six. **9** 1,500 metres. **10** The

USSR. **11** Surya Bosnaly. **12** Tony Nash and Robin Dixon. **13** Austria's Ernst Vettori. **14** Martin and Graham. **15** Bracknell and Durham. **16** The super giant slalom. **17** Garmisch-Partenkirchen in 1936. **18** Cross-country. **19** Norway's Sonja Henie. **20** The USA, Great Britain, Canada and USSR. **21** 1988 at Calgary. **22** Houses. **23** Rudi Nierlich. **24** Jean-Claude Killy, of France. **25** 1976 and 1980. **26** Austria. **27** He crashed into a snow plough while training. **28** The two man event was added to the existing four man discipline. **29** Ski-ing and shooting. **30** Canada was always represented by a club side rather than a national one.

American Football: Answers

1 $422,149. **2** Minneapolis. **3** Chicago Bears and New Orleans Saints. **4** Green Bay Packers. **5** In 1942, when it was at Durham, North Carolina. **6** Wembley Stadium. **7** They had been adopted by street gangs. **8** San Francisco 49ers and Miami Dolphins. **9** Scott Norwood. **10** Joe Montana, the 49ers quarterback. **11** New England Patriots. **12** Five. **13** Larry Kennon. **14** Oakland Raiders. **15** Honolulu, Hawaii. **16** London Monarchs. **17** 12. **18** The Crown Jewels. **19** The Sugar Bowl. **20** Minnesota Vikings. **21** They were or are all Chicago Gridiron teams. **22** 1982 and 1987. **23** A desperate pass into the end zone, aimed at a hopeful touchdown. **24** They did not win a single game in the NFL season. **25** The Houston Astrodome. **26** 35, by the Washington Redskins in the second quarter of Superbowl XXII. **27** Italy. **28** London Monarchs, Barcelona Dragons, Frankfurt Galaxy. **29** Miami. **30** Frankford YELLOWJACKETS. Providence STEAMROLLER.

Golf: Answers

1 Dave Stockton. **2** His seven iron. **3** US Masters, 1991.
4 As ninth reserve, he was only told he could compete the day before the tournament started, after Nick Price pulled out when his wife went into labour. **5** At 14,335 feet, it is the world's highest. **6** Serving wine. It is a claret jug. **7** 1971. **8** Hale Irwin. **9** Jack Nicklaus. 1965 and 1966. **10** The Old Course at St Andrews. **11** Prestwick.
12 He complained that sand in the bunker he had landed in was too soft. **13** He was the last amateur to win either championship. **14** Doug Sanders. **15** Fanny Sunesson.
16 A top hat full. **17** His son, Tom Morris Junior.
18 The USA's National Football League. **19** Wentworth. **20** 75. **21** He shot a round of 63.
22 Meg Mallon. **23** It was the first year the championship was decided by strokeplay. **24** John Hudson.
25 Kiawah Island, the Ryder Cup course. **26** He changed his scorecard. **27** Eldrick Woods. **28** Mark Mouland – he came joint 17th. **29** Nothing. He was an amateur. **30** Neil Coles. He played in 40.

Football – Part 3: Answers

1 1863. **2** Chelsea. **3** Preston, Aston Villa, Tottenham, Arsenal and Liverpool. **4** Scunthorpe United.
5 Lancaster Gate, in London. **6** Copa America. **7** 102 times. **8** Norwich City. **9** Albania. **10** 1919. **11** Old Trafford. **12** 97. **13** The Commonwealth Games.
14 PSV Eindhoven. **15** Oxford United and Reading.
16 Malcolm MacDonald. **17** 1977. **18** Ossie Ardiles and Ricardo Villa. **19** Harold Wilson. **20** Diamond Nights. **21** Juventus. **22** Ivory Coast. **23** Today newspapers and Canon. **24** Alan Shearer. **25** V f B Stuttgart. **26** The FA Cup. **27** 1970, at Mexico City.
28 South American clubs have won more. **29** Hockey.
30 Charterhouse (Old Carthusians) and Eton (Old Etonians).

Athletics - Part 3: Answers

1 Florence Griffith-Joyner. **2** Ben Jipcho. **3** 1880. **4** Heptathlon. **5** Chalford Hundred and Thames Valley Harriers. **6** Westminster Bridge. **7** The politically motivated Games of the New Emerging Forces, organised by Indonesia's President Sukarno. **8** Coventry, in 1908. **9** 25. **10** Fatima Whitbread. **11** Two man bobsleigh. **12** 5,000 metres and javelin. **13** Wendy Sly. **14** Mike Powell, of the USA, jumped 8.95 metres. **15** Seb Coe, Steve Cram and Steve Ovett. **16** Katrin Krabbe and Gwen Torrence. **17** He was the first competitor in the 32 year history of the games to test positive for anabolic steroids. **18** 100 metres. **19** Zola Budd. **20** The Niger Republic. **21** New Zealand's John Walker. **22** Liz McColgan's 10,000 metres win in the Tokyo 1991 World Championships. **23** Carl Lewis. **24** Florence. **25** 1991. **26** Two. **27** Treatment of gout. **28** 1989. **29** Oxford University's Iffley Road track. **30** She was the first athlete to fail a chromosone sex test, although she had already passed a physical examination.

Cricket - Part 3: Answers

1 Kepler Wessels. **2** Mike Gatting. **3** Ian Chappell. **4** They made 406 against the West Indies. **5** 1787. **6** East Africa. **7** Eric Hollies. **8** Ian Botham, against India in Bombay, 1979–80. **9** They were the only county side never to have reached a one day final at Lords. **10** It's an Australian term for a googly. **11** Richard Illingworth, in the third Test against West Indies at Trent Bridge. **12** Geoffrey Boycott, David Gower, Colin Cowdrey, Wally Hammond and Graham Gooch. **13** The European Cup. **14** Limited overs cricket. **15** Viv Richards and Joel Garner. **16** A world cup tournament. **17** Ian Botham. **18** 111 runs. **19** The Imperial Cricket Conference. **20** John Wright.

21 50 years old (and 320 days). **22** Graeme Pollock, in 1970. **23** All five times. **24** Gary Sobers and Lance Gibbs. **25** Angus Fraser, despite being injured for most of the season. **26** Hertfordshire. **27** Australia and New Zealand. **28** West Indies, Australia and Pakistan. **29** Martin Snedden. **30** England's disastrous 1990–91 tour of Australia.

Origins of Sports: Answers

1 Darts. **2** Holland. **3** The petrol-fuelled internal combustion engine. **4** Windsurfing. **5** William Webb Ellis. **6** Holland. **7** Basketball. **8** Rugby League. **9** A hard ball was used in the New York game and a larger soft ball in the Boston variety. **10** Table Tennis. **11** Kent and Surrey. **12** The forward pass was officially allowed. **13** Melbourne, Victoria. **14** Jeu de Paumes. **15** India. **16** Lacrosse. **17** Water skis. **18** Fleet Prison. **19** Great Britain. **20** Polo. **21** Weightlifting. **22** The London Prize Ring rules. **23** The country estates of the Duke of Beaufort, where it is believed to have originated in 1873. **24** Sweden. **25** Surfing. **26** Squash. **27** Ice hockey. **28** He wanted his male subjects to spend more time practising archery. **29** The Byerly Turk, Darley Arabian and the Godolphin Barb. **30** Sphairistike.

Superstars – Part 2: Answers

1 Walter Payton. **2** Richard Branson. **3** Mickey Rourke. **4** Football. **5** Hank Aaron, Babe Ruth and Willie Mays. **6** 1986. **7** 100 metres, 200 metres, long jump and 4 × 100 metres relay. **8** 1937–1949. **9** Shergar. **10** Australia's David Campese. **11** The US Masters, six times. **12** Alfredo di Stefano. **13** Don Bradman, at Headingly in 1930. **14** Nigel Mansell. **15** 1978. **16** Pittsburgh Penguins. **17** Cycling. **18** Nolan Ryan.

19 Pietro Mennea. 20 Sweden's Ingemar Stenmark.
21 Gary Lineker. He came tenth, earning £640,000.
22 Simon le Bon. 23 Magic Johnson. 24 Dixie
Dean. 25 80 (83 exactly). 26 They all played Tarzan in
films. 27 49. 28 USA's Bill Shoemaker. 29 Billie
Jean King. 30 Bobby Charlton.

World Champions (UK): Answers

1 1984. 2 Steve Davis, Stephen Hendry and John
Parrott. 3 Individual pursuit. 4 John Whitaker.
5 Ian Woosnam. 6 Bantamweight. 7 1988. 8 Never.
9 Tony Nash and Robin Dixon, in the two man bobsleigh. 10 The women's World Open Squash Championships. 11 Wigan. 12 Fatima Whitbread. 13 Jackie
Stewart. 14 Four. 15 1966. 16 Junior middleweight.
17 Mike Hawthorn. 18 Three times. 19 Steven
Redgrave. 20 Flyweight. 21 Honda. 22 100 metres
breaststroke and 200 metres breaststroke. 23
Croquet. 24 Table tennis. 25 Louise Aitken-Walker.
26 Bob Nudd. 27 Modern pentathlon. 28 Scotland.
29 He won it in 1897 and lost it in 1899. 30 Marbles.

Rivals: Answers

1 Lancashire and Yorkshire. 2 Hearts and Hibernian.
3 The passionate Harvard and Yale games. 4 Bernard
Gallacher, skipper of the losing Europe team.
5 1883. 6 Alain Prost and Ayrton Senna. 7 It was the
first ever semi-final to be held at Wembley.
8 Muhammad Ali and Joe Frazier. 9 66 fans died when a
crash barrier collapsed at Ibrox stadium. 10 Elisha
Scott. 11 New Zealand and Australia. 12 Steve Ovett
and Sebastian Coe. 13 The Rams and the Raiders. 14 The two managers were brothers. Tommy
McLean was manager of the winners, Motherwell, while

Jim McLean was in charge of Dundee United.
15 Australia II. **16** Chile. **17** Gillespie went to Celtic
and McCall went to Rangers. **18** The under-21 Varsity
rugby union match. **19** Five. **20** The New York Yankees and the New York Giants. **21** The Calcutta
Cup. **22** Eton and Harrow. **23** Hungary and the
USSR – it was shortly after Soviet troops had invaded
Hungary. **24** Real Madrid and Atletico Madrid. **25** In
the 1984 Milk Cup final. **26** 5,000 (5,028 exactly).
27 1877. **28** "No Mas, No Mas" (No more, no
more). **29** Australian skipper Greg ordered his brother
Trevor to bowl the final ball underarm to prevent the New
Zealand batsman from being able to score the six they
needed to tie the match. **30** The collision between Zola
Budd and Mary Decker in the much hyped showdown
between the two in the women's 3,000 metres final at the
1984 Los Angeles Olympics.

Trophies: Answers

1 An exact replica is kept in case the original is lost or
stolen. **2** The Cresta Run. **3** American Football's
Superbowl. **4** Women golfers. **5** The Doggett's Coat
and Badge, awarded to the winners of a rowing race on the
Thames. **6** Yachts. **7** Benson and Hedges. **8** Horse
racing. **9** Brazil's national football team. **10** A
belt. **11** Greyhounds. **12** Windsurfing. **13** The
International Industries Fairs Inter-Cities Cup. **14** Yetton
Trophy. **15** The Stanley Cup. **16** Polo. **17** The
Royal International Horse Show. **18** Cricket. **19** The
Varsity Rugby Union match. **20** The Swaythling Cup.
21 Australian Rules Football. **22** The season's best
college player. **23** The Constructors' Cup. **24** Henley
Regatta. **25** Shinty. **26** The Louis Vuitton Cup.
27 Badminton. **28** The man of the match in the Chal-
lenge Cup final. **29** A green jacket. **30** The Arthur
Dunn Cup.

Weird and Wonderful: Answers

1 Cuba's Fidel Castro. **2** He was chased by a female streaker. **3** Ted Heath. **4** Ludwig van Beethoven. **5** His moustache. **6** They were running along the M1 motorway. **7** For "not trying." **8** They were going to use it as a prisoner of war camp. **9** It was raining. **10** They believe the leathers contain evil spirits. **11** He kissed a member of the opposition, who had just missed an open goal. **12** Wyatt Earp. **13** Rudyard Kipling. **14** Volleyball. **15** The sinking of the Titanic. **16** Four days. **17** Only the USA competitors had entered the event. **18** Bog-snorkelling. **19** Free pizzas. **20** He was given a lift in a passing car. **21** He waited in the fog until the rest of the field came round again before galloping past to win the race. **22** Goalkeeper. **23** Making faces. **24** He fell onto a cactus. **25** The Titanic. **26** He was only 5ft 3ins tall. **27** The Greyhound Grand National. **28** Bram Stoker, the creator of Dracula. **29** It was 100 metres down a mine. **30** They were all British policemen.

Other Boxtree Quiz Books

THE COUNTDOWN PUZZLE BOOK
Fun word and number games for all the family based on the popular TV game show, *Countdown*. Games featured include letter games, conundrums, 'weird' wordsearches, crossword puzzles, pun fun, word ladders – and they are played against the clock.

ISBN: 1–85283–072–7

15–1 SUPERCHALLENGE
Based on Channel 4's popular general knowledge quiz show, *15–1*, this book tests your knowledge of a wide range of subjects. The final round is extremely demanding – making this book a true Superchallenge! Ideal for pub quiz nights or family fun.

ISBN: 1–85283–135–9

THE $64,000 QUESTION QUIZ BOOK
The $64,000 Question is the game show with the biggest cash prize on British TV and the toughest questions for those with enough nerve to join quizmaster, Bob Monkhouse, under the spotlight. This book contains general knowledge questions, each round more difficult than the last.

ISBN: 1–85283–695–4

THE KRYPTON FACTOR
Based on television's toughest quiz show, this book tests your intelligence, mental agility and general knowledge. Have you got what it takes to meet the *Krypton Factor* challenge?

ISBN: 1–85283–266–5